VOYAGES
RESEARCH-BASED MATHEMATICS

GRADE 4

Subtopic Assessments

Developed by
The School District of Hillsborough County
and
Metropolitan Teaching and Learning Company

SENIOR AUTHORS
AL SORIANO, JACK BEERS

SENIOR AUTHORS
Albert Soriano, Jr.
Supervisor, Elementary Mathematics (retired)
School District of Hillsborough County

Jack Beers
Vice President, Math and Science
Metropolitan Teaching and
Learning Company

AUTHOR, K–5; PROGRAM MANAGER, K–2
Janet White
Elementary Mathematics
School District of Hillsborough County

AUTHOR, K–5; PROGRAM MANAGER, 3–5
John Fahle
Elementary Mathematics
School District of Hillsborough County

AUTHOR, K–5; TECHNICAL DESIGN MANAGER, K–5
Keith Aborn
Elementary Mathematics
School District of Hillsborough County

AUTHOR, K–5; LEAD KINDERGARTEN CONSULTANT
Barbara Knox
Elementary Mathematics
School District of Hillsborough County

AUTHORS, SCHOOL DISTRICT OF HILLSBOROUGH COUNTY
Michelle Vela
Deborah Huff
Susan Crescentini
Arlyn Colley
Diane Fojaco
Susan Cox

CONTRIBUTING AUTHOR/EDITOR, SCHOOL DISTRICT OF HILLSBOROUGH COUNTY
Marian Whitehurst

CONTRIBUTING RESOURCE TEACHERS, ELEMENTARY MATHEMATICS, SCHOOL DISTRICT OF HILLSBOROUGH COUNTY
Rita Dugan
Elizabeth Glenn (retired)

SCHOOL DISTRICT OF HILLSBOROUGH COUNTY

Metropolitan Teaching and Learning Company
33 Irving Place
New York, NY 10003

ISBN 1-58120-668-2

1 2 3 4 5 6 7 8 9 DBH 06 05 04 03

Table of Contents

Topic 1, Subtopic 1 Assessment:
Data and Bar Graphs

Use the information and data chart below to answer questions 1 and 2.

Denny and Annie keep a dive log. The length of a dive represents the actual amount of time the diver spends underwater.

DIVE LOG

Diver	Length of Dive #1	Length of Dive #2	Length of Dive #3	Length of Dive #4
Denny	25 min	35 min	25 min	30 min
Annie	30 min	45 min	20 min	45 min

❶ If the data in the chart were displayed using a double-bar graph, which piece of data would have the shortest bar?

    A. Denny's dive #1   **C.** Annie's dive #3

    B. Annie's dive #1   **D.** Denny's dive #4

❷ Which graph below best represents the data in the chart?

F.

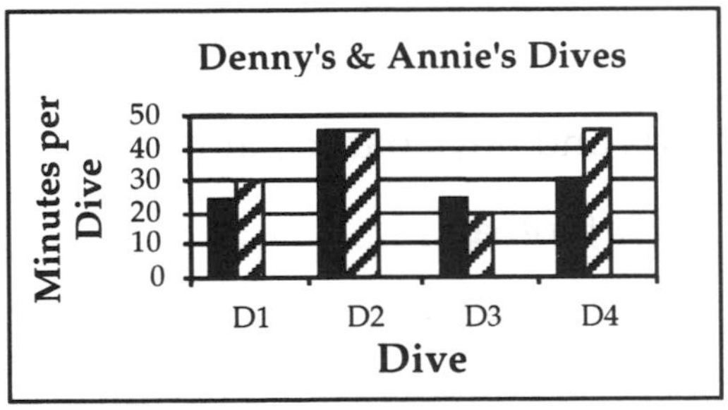

Denny's & Annie's Dives

Minutes per Dive

50 40 30 20 10 0

D1 D2 D3 D4

Dive

H.

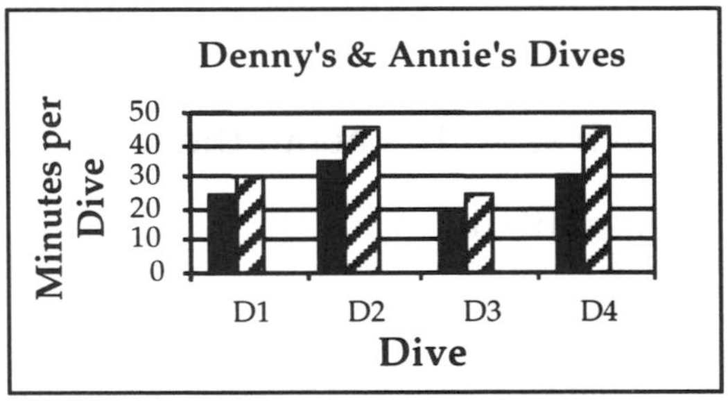

Denny's & Annie's Dives

Minutes per Dive

50 40 30 20 10 0

D1 D2 D3 D4

Dive

G.

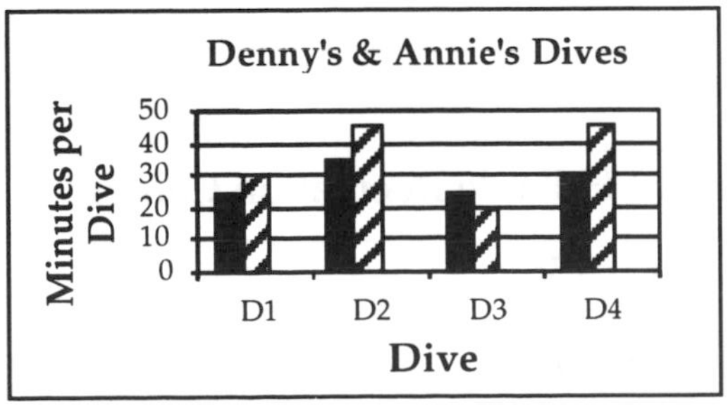

Denny's & Annie's Dives

Minutes per Dive

50 40 30 20 10 0

D1 D2 D3 D4

Dive

I.

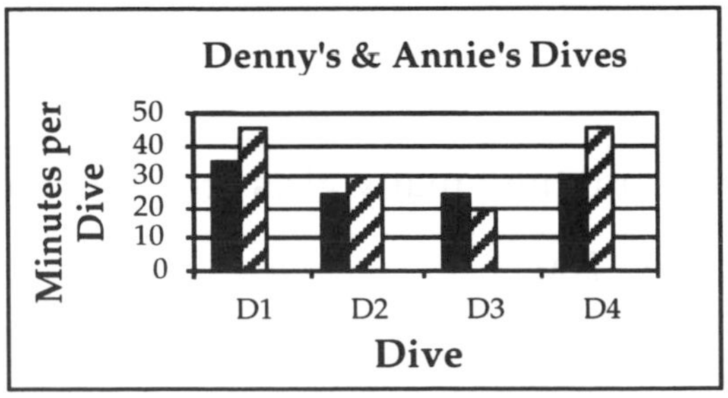

Denny's & Annie's Dives

Minutes per Dive

50 40 30 20 10 0

D1 D2 D3 D4

Dive

KEY

Denny

Annie

Topic 1, Subtopic 1: Page 1

Use the following data table and graph to answer questions 9 and 10.

PRICE COMPARISON FOR TWO ELECTRONICS STORES

Store	Spinco CD/DVD Player	Bigview TV	Sorse Video Game System	Sonic 4 Surround-Sound Stereo System
Electronics Universe	$150.00	$475.00	$225.00	$425.00
Audio/Video World	$125.00	$525.00	$275.00	$500.00

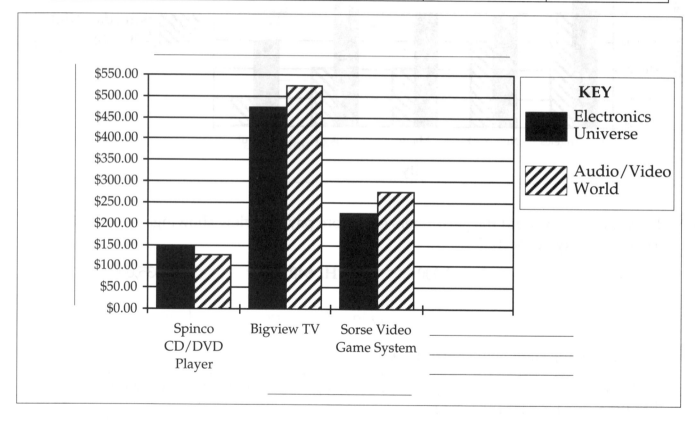

9 Using the information in the data table, fill in the missing bars, the title, and the labels for each axis on the graph above.

10 Write two comparison statements based on the information in the graph.

1. _____

2. _____

Name: _____ Grade: 4

Topic 1, Subtopic 2 Assessment:
Circle Graphs and Line Graphs

Use the following information to answer questions 1 and 2.

Knot's Elementary has a student council. The line graph shows the activity of their school improvement fund.

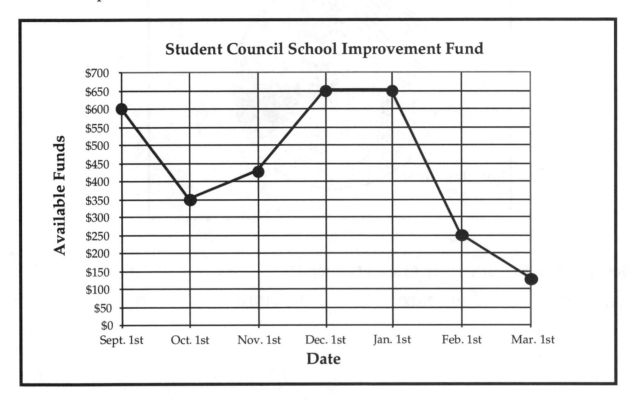

Student Council School Improvement Fund

❶ During which time period did the student council's available funds increase the most?

    A. Sept. 1st to Oct. 1st   **C.** Nov. 1st to Dec. 1st

    B. Oct. 1st to Nov. 1st   **D.** Dec. 1st to Jan. 1st

❷ What is the interval on the vertical axis of this line graph?

    F. $700.00   **H.** one Month

    G. $50.00   **I.** six Months

Use the following information to answer questions 3-5.

Adrien made the circle graph to show how she was planning on spending the $100 she earned walking dogs this summer.

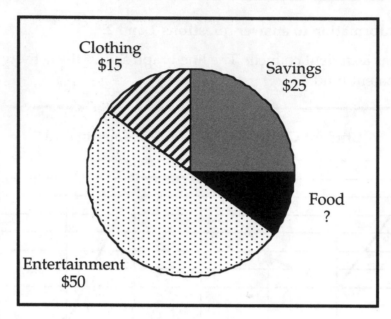

3 How much does Adrien plan to spend on food?

    A. $25.00   **B.** $20.00   **C.** $15.00   **D.** $10.00

4 What fraction of the money is Adrien planning to spend?

    F. $\frac{3}{4}$ **G.** $\frac{1}{2}$ **H.** $\frac{1}{4}$ **I.** $\frac{1}{10}$

5 What is a good title for the circle graph?

    A. Why Adrien Should Save More   **C.** Walking Dogs

    B. Too Many Parties   **D.** Adrien's $100 Budget

Name: _____

Use the graph to answer questions 6-8.

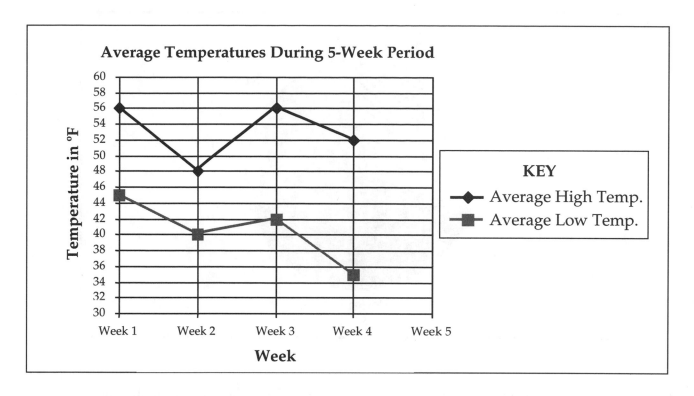

6 During which week was the average high temperature farthest from the average low temperature?

    F. Week 1   **G.** Week 2   **H.** Week 3   **I.** Week 4

7 Is the following statement true or false?

During week 3, the average high temperature was 7 degrees warmer than the average low temperature.

True or false? _____

Explain your thinking. _____

_____

8 During week 5 the average high temperature was 55° F and the average low was 38° F. Complete the above line graph to show this data accurately.

Use the information below to answer questions 9 and 10.

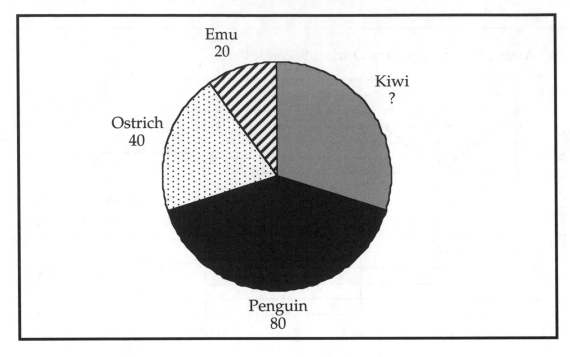

Miguel surveyed all 200 students in the fifth grade to find the most popular flightless bird they studied in science class. The circle graph shows the results of his survey.

9 How many 5th graders voted for Kiwi as the most popular flightless bird? _____

Explain your thinking. _____

_____

10 **10.a.** Write a title for the circle graph. _____

10.b. Write a survey question that Miguel might have asked the 5th graders in order to collect his data. _____

_____

Topic 1, Subtopic 3 Assessment:
Using Graphs

❶ Which type of graph would be the most useful in showing a trend over time?

    A. bar graph   **C.** line graph

    B. circle graph   **D.** pictograph

Use the information to answer questions 2 and 3.

Theo made the data table below after interviewing some police officers and firefighters. He asked them what they felt was the busiest time of day for them at work.

SOME BUSY TIMES FOR PUBLIC SERVANTS

Group Interviewed	Morning	Afternoon	Night
Police Officers	26	13	61
Firefighters	32	21	47

❷ Which type of graph would be best to show the data in the above table?

    F. single-bar graph   **H.** circle graph

    G. pictograph   **I.** double-bar graph

❸ Which information can be found using the data?

    A. The number of firefighters in Theo's town.

    B. The time of day the police officers were interviewed.

    C. The time of day the police officers interviewed were busiest.

    D. The least busy day of the week for the firefighters that were interviewed.

Use the following information for questions 4-7.

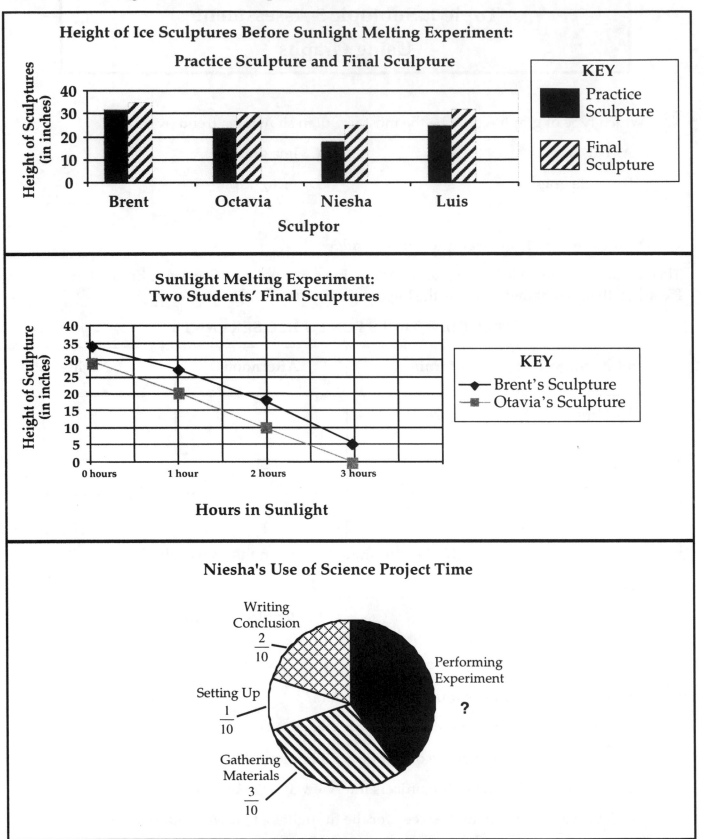

Height of Ice Sculptures Before Sunlight Melting Experiment:

Practice Sculpture and Final Sculpture

KEY
- Practice Sculpture
- Final Sculpture

Height of Sculptures (in inches)

Brent   Octavia   Niesha   Luis

Sculptor

Sunlight Melting Experiment:
Two Students' Final Sculptures

Height of Sculpture (in inches)

0 hours   1 hour   2 hours   3 hours

Hours in Sunlight

KEY
- Brent's Sculpture
- Otavia's Sculpture

Niesha's Use of Science Project Time

Writing Conclusion $\frac{2}{10}$

Setting Up $\frac{1}{10}$

Gathering Materials $\frac{3}{10}$

Performing Experiment

?

Name: _____

Use the graphs on the previous page to answer questions 4-7.

❹ Which student had the second tallest final ice sculpture before the melting experiment began?

  F. Brent   **G.** Luis   **H.** Niesha   **I.** Octavia

❺ How tall was Octavia's ice sculpture after three hours in the sunlight?

  A. zero inches   **C.** twenty-one inches

  B. eight inches   **D.** thirty inches

❻ Which graph shows the height of Niesha's final ice sculpture after it had been in the sunlight for one hour?

  F. double-bar graph   **H.** circle graph

  G. double-line graph   **I.** none of the graphs

❼ Is the following statement true or false?

  | Niesha spent over half her time performing the experiment and writing a conclusion. |

  True or false? _____

  Explain your thinking. _____

  _____

  _____

  _____

  _____

Use the data table and line graph to answer questions 8-10.

Student's Collection	1999	2000	2001	2002
Jill	$150	$210	$325	$480
Raven	$320	$390	$415	$440

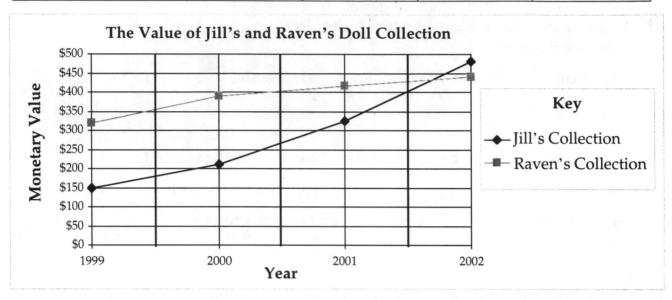

The Value of Jill's and Raven's Doll Collection

8 Why do you think that a line graph was used to show the data? _____

_____

_____

9 The information in the graph is accurate. Is the data table accurate? _____

Explain your thinking. _____

_____

_____

10 If the trend for both doll collections continues, what would you say about the values of the collections in the year 2003? _____

Explain your thinking. _____

_____

_____

Topic 2, Subtopic 1 Assessment:
Place Value

Use the place value chart to answer questions 1 and 2.

hundred thousands	ten thousands	thousands	,	hundreds	tens	ones
8	9	0		6	2	7

1 What number is written in the chart?

　A. eighty-nine thousand six hundred twenty-seven

　B. eight hundred ninety-six thousand twenty-seven

　C. eight hundred ninety thousand six hundred twenty-seven

　D. eight million nine hundred sixty-two thousand seven

2 Which number represents the value of the 9 in the chart?

　F. 90

　G. 900

　H. 9,000

　I. 90,000

3 Which expanded form number is equal to 426,807?

　A. 40,000 + 2,000 + 600 + 80 + 7

　B. 400,000 + 20,000 + 6,000 + 800 + 70

　C. 400,000 + 20,000 + 6,000 + 800 + 7

　D. 4,000,000 + 200,000 + 60,000 + 8,000 + 7

Use the following table to answer question 4.

Roman Numeral	Value
I	1
V	5
X	10
L	50
C	100
D	500
M	1,000

4 What is the value of the Roman numeral MCLIX?

    F. 1,611   **G.** 1,609   **H.** 1,159   **I.** 1,141

5 Compare the base ten number below with the base five number. Which symbol makes the statement correct?

$$14_{ten} \bigcirc 24_{five}$$

    A. <   **C.** =

    B. >   **D.** none of the above

Name: _____

6 Use the incomplete expanded form number below to answer the question.

$$2,000,000 + 7,000 + 100 + 70 + 8$$

Which value is needed in the expanded form so that the number above is equal to 2,407,178?

F. 400

G. 4,000

H. 40,000

I. 400,000

7 Is this statement true or false?

5,192,087 in word form is five million, one hundred ninety-two thousand and eighty-seven hundredths.

True or false? _____

Explain your thinking. _____

_____

8 Is the following statement true or false?

The value of the 4 in the number 748,395 is equal to 4 x 1,000.

True or false? _____

Explain your thinking. _____

_____

9 Use these illustrations to answer the questions below.

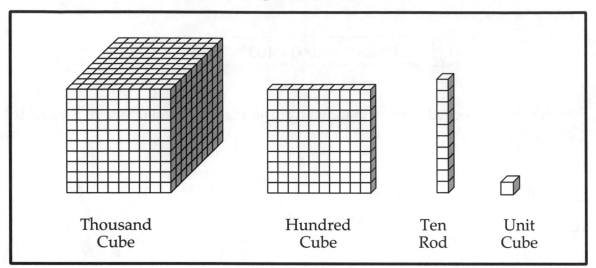

Thousand Cube   Hundred Cube   Ten Rod   Unit Cube

You have the following manipulatives:

6 thousand cubes   **15 hundred flats**

7 ten rods   **8 unit cubes**

9.a. Write in expanded form, the combined value of all of the manipulatives shown in the box.

Answer: _____

9.b. If the value of the hundred flat is n, what is the value of the thousand cube? _____

10 Circle the number forms below that represent the same numerical value.

- Sixty thousand three hundred seventy-four

- $(6 \times 10{,}000) + (3 \times 1{,}000) + (7 \times 100) + (4 \times 10) + (4 \times 1)$

- $60{,}000 + 3{,}000 + 700 + 4$

- $60{,}374$

Topic 2, Subtopic 2 Assessment:
Comparing and Ordering Whole Numbers

❶ Which point on the number line most likely represents the number 4,650?

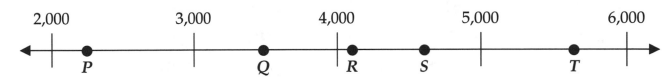

A. Point *T*   C. Point *R*

B. Point *S*   D. Point *Q*

❷ Troy always rounded to the nearest 1,000 when ordering supplies.
If he rounded the order to 8,000, on which actual amount did he base his order?

F. 8,920   H. 7,722

G. 8,708   I. 7,344

❸ Violet needed a close approximation of the number $273.78 so she rounded
to the nearest dollar. Which is the correct amount?

A. $274.00   C. $270.00

B. $273.00   D. $264.00

4 Jack, Janet, Keith, and Barbara had a contest to see who could order a group of numbers greatest to least. Below are their results. Which contestant ordered the numbers correctly, **greatest** to **least**?

F.	Barbara:	3,476	4,367	4,763	3,746
G.	Keith:	4,763	4,367	3,476	3,746
H.	Jack:	4,367	4,763	3,746	3,476
I.	Janet:	4,763	4,367	3,746	3,476

5 Tran was comparing his card collections to his friend's collections. Which comparison is correct?

A. 676 baseball cards   <   667 baseball cards

B. 547 hockey cards   >   574 hockey cards

C. 404 football cards   <   444 football cards

D. 367 soccer cards   =   376 hockey cards

6 Which number is missing from the sequence listed below?

12,500	12,750	13,000	_____	13,500	13,750

F. 13,150   H. 13,350

G. 13,250   I. 13,450

Name: _____

7 Is this statement true or false?

15,969 rounded to the nearest hundred is 16,000.

True or false? _____

Explain your thinking. _____

_____

8 Insert the correct symbol (<, >, =) for each equality or inequality.

8a. 2,845 $\bigcirc$ two thousand eight hundred five

8b. 32,983 $\bigcirc$ 30,000 + 2,000 + 900 + 90

8c. 765,894 $\bigcirc$ 756,849

9 Write the following list of numbers in order from **least** to **greatest.**

17,630   16,703   71,673   16,307   67,630

_____   _____   _____   _____   _____

10 Mark a point and its letter on the number line to show the approximate location of each number. The first one is done for you.

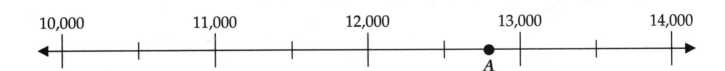

12,800: *A*   10,400: *B*   13,550: *C*   11,100: *D*

10,000   11,000   12,000   13,000   14,000

A

Topic 2, Subtopic 3 Assessment:
Adding and Subtracting Whole Numbers

Use the data table below to answer questions 1-3.

The table shows the number of schools in some of Florida's largest school districts.

2001-2002 NUMBER OF SCHOOLS PER COUNTY SCHOOL DISTRICT

Broward	Dade	Hillsborough	Orange	Palm Beach
247	418	241	185	218

❶ How many more schools are in the Dade County School District than the Broward County School District?

   A. 171   **B.** 213   **C.** 247   **D.** 665

❷ Find the districts showing the greatest and least number of schools. How many schools do these two districts have altogether?

   F. 603 schools   **G.** 465 schools   **H.** 418 schools   **I.** 233 schools

❸ Which two school districts combined have a total of 403 schools?

   A. Broward and Hillsborough

   B. Dade and Broward

   C. Hillsborough and Palm Beach

   D. Orange and Palm Beach

4 In 1927, Charles Lindbergh made the first non-stop flight across the Atlantic. Forty-two years later, the first men walked on the moon. In what year did the astronauts first land on the moon?

F. 1959

G. 1962

H. 1969

I. 1972

5 The Best of Bargains outlet store has a display of 248 scented candles, 395 unscented candles, and 146 colored light bulbs. How many candles are on display at the outlet store?

A. 789 candles

B. 643 candles

C. 533 candles

D. 147 candles

6 The Long Beach Recreation obstacle course is 632 feet long. The North Beach obstacle course is 149 feet shorter. The Highland Beach obstacle course is 437 feet long. The racers make a prediction about the length of the North Beach Course. Which statement is correct?

F. The North Beach Course is 149 feet long.

G. The North Beach Course is 437 feet long.

H. The North Beach Course is between 632 feet and 149 feet long.

I. The North Beach Course is greater than 632 feet long.

Name: _____

7 The warehouse had 3,250 crates in storage on Sunday. Monday, another 450 crates arrived. Tuesday, 230 crates were delivered from the warehouse to an electrical supply store. How many crates are still in the warehouse?

Is the following statement true or false?

The number sentence for solving this problem could be:
$3,250 + 450 + 230 = 3,930$

True or false? _____

How many crates are still in the warehouse? _____

Explain your thinking. _____

_____

_____

8 The following are examples that represent the Commutative Property of Addition.

$47 + 21 = 21 + 47$
$1,495 + 2,380 = 2,380 + 1,495$

Explain the meaning of the Commutative Property. _____

_____

_____

9 Fill in the rectangle to make each number sentence true.

9a. $\boxed{} - 32 = 90$

9b. $2,624 + \boxed{} = 3,955$

9c. $438 + \boxed{} + 274 = 900$

10 Ito was involved in a contest to find the longest time a person could stay up on a unicycle. Look at the time schedule below that shows Ito's contest results.

ITO'S CONTEST RESULTS

On Unicycle	Break	On Unicycle	Break and Lunch	On Unicycle	Break	On Unicycle
47 min	10 min	36 min	20 min	49 min	10 min	58 min

How long was Ito actually on the unicycle during the entire contest? _____

Show your work.

Topic 2, Subtopic 4 Assessment:
Estimating Sums and Differences

❶ The Summer Fun concert at Stingray Beach had 6,730 people in attendance.
The Hot Nights concert at Stingray Beach had 12,372 people in attendance.
About how many people attended the two concerts altogether?

A. 5,000   C. 20,000

B. 10,000   D. 30,000

❷ Pavement Pete's parking garage holds seven hundred ninety-seven cars.
Auto Accommodation's parking garage holds three hundred fifteen cars.
About how many more parking places are in Pavement Pete's garage?

F. 500   H. 1,000

G. 800   I. 4,000

❸ About 238,000 people were spectators at the parade. About 372,000 people
watched the parade on television. What is the closest estimate of the difference
between the number of people who watched the parade on television and the number
who were there in person?

A. 500,000   C. 130,000

B. 200,000   D. 13,000

Use the information below to answer questions 4-6.

SUPREME SPORTING SURPLUS STORE

Item	Price (per item)
Tent	$46.21
Fishing Pole	$35.85
Basketball	$11.98
Soccer Ball	$18.75
Tennis Racquet	$21.97
Running Sneakers	$73.56
Skateboard	$44.39
Bat	$14.56

4 Which would be the estimate for the cost of a skateboard and a tent if you used front-end estimation?

    F. $60.00   **H.** $100.00

    G. $80.00   **I.** $120.00

5 About how much more do running sneakers cost than a basketball?

    A. $90.00   **C.** $30.00

    B. $60.00   **D.** $10.00

6 In order to get a close estimate for the cost of bat, a fishing pole, and a soccer ball, Sergio rounded each to the nearest dollar before figuring the total cost. What was Sergio's estimate?

    F. $60.00   **H.** $70.00

    G. $65.00   **I.** $75.00

Name: _____

❼ Jamie bought one pair of shoes for $29.00 and another pair for $37.00.

Is this statement true or false?

$50.00 is a good estimate of the total amount that Jamie spent.

True or false? _____

Explain your thinking. _____

_____

❽ Joanne is estimating the combined land area of Texas and Alaska, the two largest states. She needs to know only whether the combined area is greater than or less than a million square miles. The area of Texas is 268,601 square miles. The area of Alaska is 656,425 square miles.

Explain which estimation strategy she should use for her situation and why.

_____

_____

_____

❾ Cyrus calculates the difference in length between the longest subaqueous (below a body of water) road tunnel in Japan and in the United States.

Tokyo Wan Aqua-Line (Japan)	9,583 meters
Brooklyn Battery Tunnel (USA)	2,779 meters

Cyrus predicts that the difference will be less than 9,583.

Is his prediction reasonable? _____

Explain your thinking. _____

_____

_____

⑩ Use the information in the map to answer the questions below.

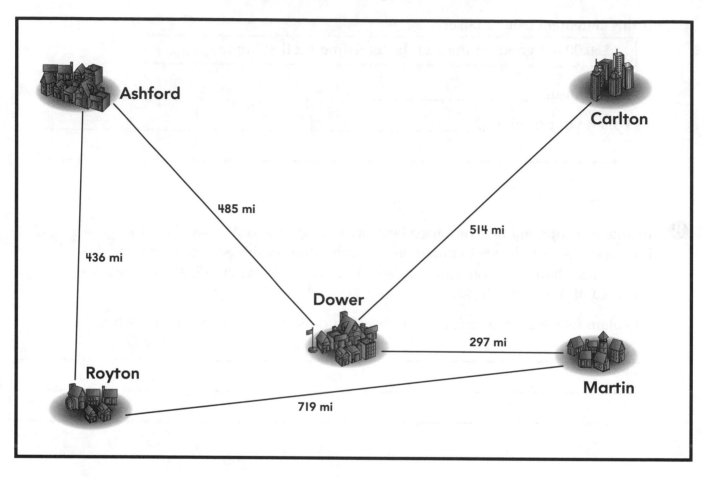

Use the strategy listed to solve each problem.

10a. About how far is it from Ashford to Martin, passing through Royton?

Front-end estimation: _____

10b. About how much further is it from Royton to Martin than from Dower to Martin?

Rounding to the nearest ten: _____

10c. About how far is the shortest route shown from Carlton to Ashford?

Compatible numbers: _____

Topic 2, Subtopic 5 Assessment:
Algebraic Concepts

❶ What is the pattern for the sequence of numbers listed below?

3, 6, 7, 13, 4, 21, 22, 41

    A. add 3, subtract 1

    B. subtract 3, add 1

    C. multiply by 2, add 1

    D. there is no repeating pattern

❷ What are the numbers missing from the following sequence?

13, 10, 19, 16, 25, 22, _____ , _____ , 37, 34, 43

Hint: The rule uses two operations, addition and subtraction.

    F. 31 and 28

    G. 25 and 34

    H. 19 and 28

    I. 13 and 16

❸ What is the rule for the table?

Input (n)	1,450	2,450	3,450	4,450	5,450
Output	925	1,925	2,925	3,925	4,925

    A. $n + 925$

    B. $n - 925$

    C. $n - 525$

    D. $n + 1450$

4 Which equation is true?

    F. $61 + 29 = 120 - 15$

    G. $17 + 38 = 22 + 43$

    H. $340 - 70 = 200 + 90$

    I. $160 + 70 = 300 - 70$

5 Use the balance and the rules to answer the question below.

    Rule 1:   All like shapes have the same value.

    Rule 2:   Unlike shapes do not have the same value.

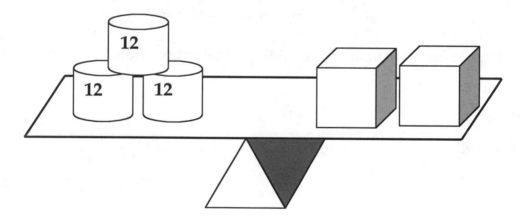

What is the value of one cube?

    A. 36

    B. 18

    C. 12

    D. 6

6 There were 210 people standing in line. By 4:00 P.M., *n* number of people joined the line. There are now 315 people in the line. Which equation expresses this scenario?

    F. $210 - n = 315$

    G. $210 + n = 315$

    H. $n - 315 = 210$

    I. $n \times 210 = 315$

7 Is the following statement true or false?

$$42 - 14 > 28$$

True or false?   _____

Explain your thinking. _____

_____

8 Fill in the squares with the appropriate weights to make the balance even. Use each weight only once.

List of weights:		
8 grams	26 grams	17 grams
5 grams	30 grams	

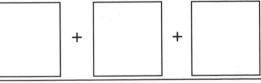 

9 Sheila withdrew $45.00 from her savings account at the bank. She bought a music CD for a certain amount of money (*m*). Sheila then gave the $28.00 she had left to her mom for safekeeping. How much did the music CD cost?

Write an equation, using the variable *m*, that could be used to solve the story problem.

_____

10 Find the pattern and then complete the table. Write the rule, using the variable *n*, for the pattern in the function table.

Hint: The rule uses two operations, multiplication and addition.

Input (*n*)	Output
2	7
4	11
6	15
8	
10	

Rule: _____

Explain your thinking. _____

_____

Topic 2, Subtopic 6 Assessment:
Decimals

Use the following number to answer questions 1 and 2.

$$6{,}423.15$$

❶ Which digit is in the tenths place?

    A. 1   **C.** 3

    B. 2   **D.** 5

❷ What is the value of the 5?

    F. $\dfrac{5}{10}$ **H.** $\dfrac{5}{100}$

    G. $\dfrac{1}{5}$ **I.** $\dfrac{1}{50}$

❸ Use the model to answer the question.

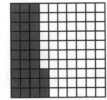 

Which equation represents the sum (*n*) of the shaded parts of the model?

    A. $0.43 + 0.45 = n$ **C.** $0.67 + 0.44 = n$

    B. $0.33 + 0.46 = n$ **D.** $0.13 + 0.56 = n$

4 Thursday, 0.07 inch of rain fell in Driebed Valley. Friday, $\frac{25}{100}$ inch of rain fell in the same location. How much rain fell overall on the two days in Driebed Valley?

    F. 0.17 inch   **H.** 0.94 inch

    G. 0.32 inch   **I.** 7.24 inches

5 Which list of decimals is ordered **least** to **greatest**?

    A. 0.09   0.2   0.40   0.73   0.92

    B. 0.3   0.07   0.77   0.09   0.92

    C. 0.08   0.03   0.12   0.34   0.05

    D. 0.92   0.73   0.40   0.2   0.09

6 Which number sentence is most likely represented on the number line?

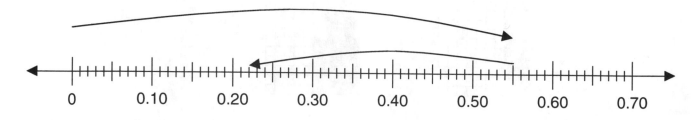

    F. 0 + 0.22 = 0.55   **H.** 0.55 – 0.33 = 0.22

    G. 0.22 + 0.55 = 0.77   **I.** 55 – 22 = 33

Name: _____

7 Is the statement true or false?

> The number 48.25 is read forty-eight hundredth twenty five.

True or false? _____

Explain your thinking. _____

_____

8 Adam traveled 0.65 km on his bicycle.

B.J. traveled 0.75 km on hers.

Carrie traveled 1.40 km on her bicycle.

Darby traveled 1.4 km on his.

Mark a point and its letter on the number line to show how far each cyclist traveled.

> Adam: *A* B.J.: *B* Carrie: *C* Darby: *D*

The first one is done for you.

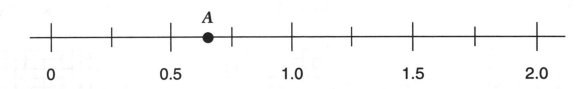

Who traveled the farthest? _____

9 Bill found a quarter, a nickel, a dime, a half-dollar, and 2 pennies in a shoebox that was sitting in the back of his closet. Write the decimal number that represents each coin he found. One of them is done for you.

Half-dollar	Quarter	Dime	Nickel	Penny	Penny
_____	_____	0.1	_____	_____	_____

How much money does Bill have? _____

10 Use the following information to respond to the problem.

> Mike's garden covers 0.29 of his backyard.
>
> Eva's patio covers 0.09 of her backyard.
>
> May's pool covers 0.58 of her backyard.

Each backyard is laid out as a 100 grid. Shade in the appropriate area for each scenario.

10a. Mike's Backyard   **10b.** Eva's Backyard   **10c.** May's Backyard

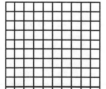   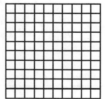   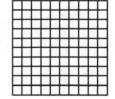

Topic 3, Subtopic 1 Assessment:
Transformations

❶ Which shape shows how the trapezoid would look after a flip over the dotted line?

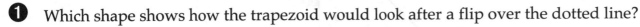
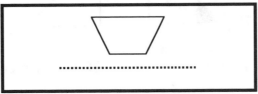

A.   B.   C.   D.

❷ Which shape below shows how the figure would look after a 180° turn?

F.   G.   H.   I.

❸ Which transformation below shows a translation?

A.

C.

B.

D.

4 Which description correctly identifies the rotation below?

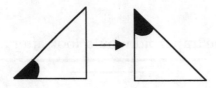

F. 90° turn counterclockwise

H. 90° turn clockwise

G. 180° turn clockwise

I. 180° turn clockwise

5 Which transformation would change the appearance of the figure below?

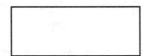

A. 360° counterclockwise turn

C. Translation

B. 90° clockwise rotation

D. 360° clockwise rotation

6 Which two words below have the same meaning?

F. Reflection – Slide

H. Turn – Translation

G. Flip – Rotation

I. Rotation – Turn

Name: _____

7 Is the statement below true or false?

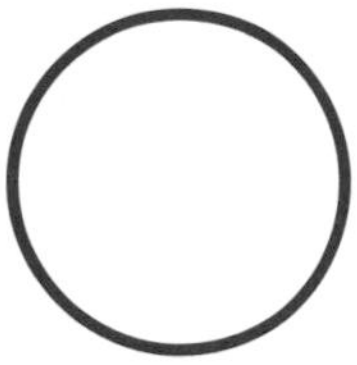

The figure above would NOT change appearance after being rotated, translated, or reflected.

True or false? _____

Explain your thinking. _____

_____

8 Which transformation will allow the shape below to fit into the vacant space of the tile floor?

Transformation: _____

9 Draw a second arrow rotated a quarter turn clockwise around the point.

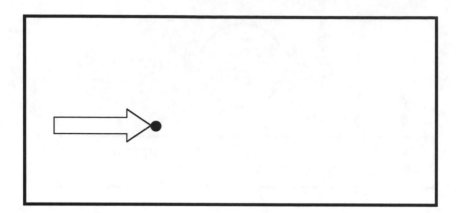

10 Draw a second parallelogram showing a flip over the dotted line. Place the dot in your figure in the correct place.

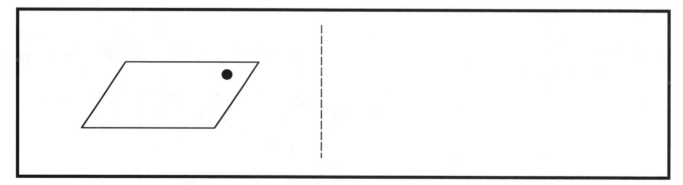

Topic 3, Subtopic 2 Assessment:
Plane Figures

Use the following diagram to answer question 1.

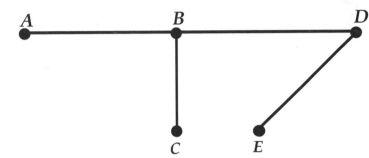

1 Which angle is a 180° angle?

   A. angle *ABC*   **C.** angle *BDE*

   B. angle *ABD*   **D.** angle *CBD*

2 Which figure has perpendicular line segments?

  F.

  G.

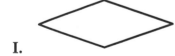

  H.

  I.

❸ Which of the following is a closed figure?

A.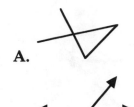

B.

C.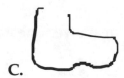

D.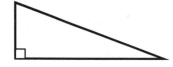

❹ Which description best fits the figure shown?

F. All my sides are congruent.

G. I am a one-dimensional figure.

H. I have one right angle.

I. Two of my angles have measures greater than 90°.

❺ Which of the following is a hexagon?

A.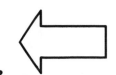

B.

C.

D.

6 Which is a true statement about a quadrilateral?

    F. There are always four 90° interior angles.

    G. The sides must be congruent and parallel.

    H. It is a six-sided polygon with six vertices.

    I. It is a four-sided closed figure.

7 Is the following statement true or false?

All polygons have at least three vertices.

True or false? _____

Explain your thinking. _____

_____

8 Circle all the statements that are true about a square.

- It is a quadrilateral.
- It is an open figure.

- It is a type of triangle.
- It is a parallelogram.

- It has exactly four angles with measures less than 90°.
- It is a special type of rectangle.

- It is a two-dimensional figure.
- It has no congruent sides.

9 Draw hands on the clock to show a 90 degree angle.

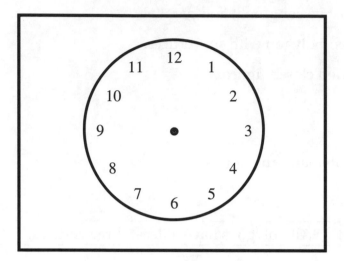

10 Use a ruler or a straight edge. Draw a closed figure made up of 5 line segments. What type of polygon is this figure?

Type of Polygon: _____

Name: _____   Grade: 4

Topic 3, Subtopic 3 Assessment:
Congruency, Similarity, Symmetry, and Grids

---

❶ Which figure has more than one line of symmetry?

A. 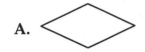   B.   C.   D.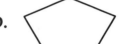

❷ Which figure is most likely congruent to the example shown?

Example:

F.   G.   H.   I.

❸ Which of the capital letters below are symmetrical?

A	F	J	L	M

A. A and M   **B.** A and L   **C.** F and J   **D.** F and L

❹ Joey took a 4"x 5" photograph to the photo store. He had it made into a 8"x 10" print.
Which geometric concept best describes the relationship between the two prints?

F. Congruency   **G.** Linear   **H.** Similarity   **I.** Symmetry

The following is a location grid posted at many sites in the Slip and Slide Water Park. Use the grid to answer questions 5-8.

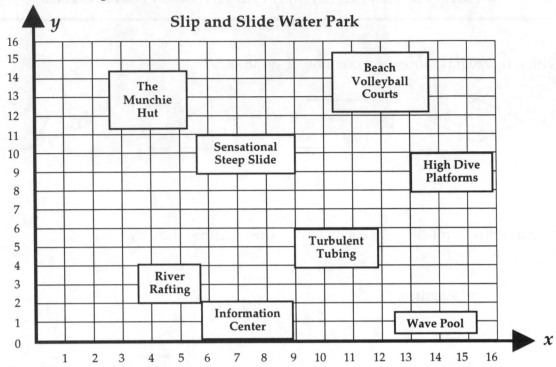

5 Percy is on the volleyball court. At what coordinates could Percy be found?

    A. (10, 15)   **B.** (11, 11)   **C.** (13, 14)   **D.** (14, 13)

6 Which one of the following items would most likely be in use at coordinates (10, 5)?

    F. beach ball   **G.** slide   **H.** raft   **I.** tube

7 Carol is standing at coordinates (14, 4). Is the following statement true or false?

> Carol is working at the Munchie Hut.

True or false? _____

Explain your thinking. _____

_____

8 Lolita told Nina to meet her at coordinates (8, 7) by 1:30 P.M. Look at the grid on the previous page. Draw a star on the location grid where Nina should meet her.

9 Use the grid below and a straightedge to solve.

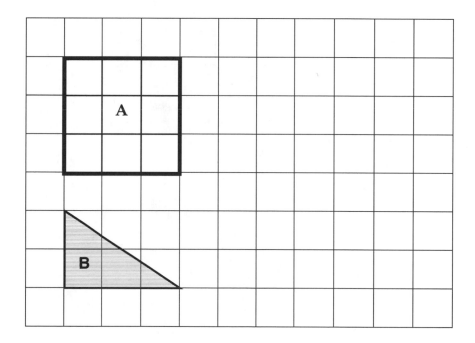

In the grid, draw a figure similar to figure A.

In the grid, draw a figure congruent to figure B.

⑩ Draw all the lines of symmetry for the figure below.

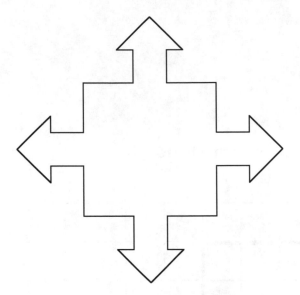

Topic 3, Subtopic 4 Assessment:
Linear Measure

❶ If you attached the three line segments end-to-end how many centimeters long would the newly formed line segment be?

A. 17 cm   B. 14 cm   C. about 11 cm   D. $6\frac{1}{2}$ cm

❷ Nathan measured the length of the public pool at the community center. Which length did he most likely find?

F. 25 centimeters   H. 25 meters

G. 25 inches   I. 25 miles

❸ Which metric unit is most appropriate for measuring the distance between two towns?

A. kilometer   C. meter

B. kilogram   D. millimeter

You will need an inch ruler and this diagram for question 4.

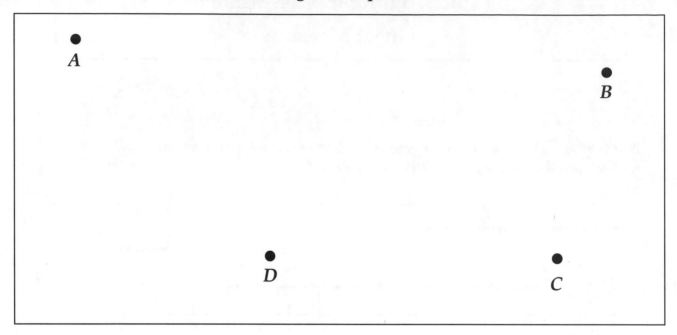

4 How many inches is it from point A to point C?

F. about 4 inches

G. $4\frac{1}{2}$ inches

H. 14 inches

I. $5\frac{1}{2}$ inches

Use the function table to answer questions 5 and 6.

Input (n)	Output
1 meter	100 centimeters
2 meters	200 centimeters
3 meters	300 centimeters
4 meters	
5 meters	

1 meter = 100 centimeters

5 How many centimeters are in 5 meters?

A. 305

B. 405

C. 450

D. 500

❻   Look at the table on the previous page. How many centimeters are in 10 meters?

  F. 10,000   **H.** 100

  G. 1,000   **I.** 10

❼

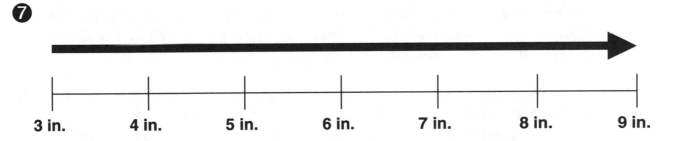

Based on the drawing above, is the following statement true or false?

| The arrow is about nine inches long. |

True or false? _____

Explain your thinking. _____

_____

Use the word bank below to answer questions 8 and 9. Fill in the space in each statement. Look under each space for the measurement system used.

meters	inches	miles	yards
centimeters	millimeters	kilometers	feet

❽

8a. Jerry measures the thickness of a nickel. He discovers that it is about two _____ thick.
        (metric)

8b. Chelsea saw an adult giraffe at the zoo. It was almost 17 _____ tall.
        (customary)

❾

9a. Hector's friend Carl sailed on a ship across the Atlantic Ocean. The trip took many days. Using a map, Carl showed the distance he traveled. The distance the ship traveled was about 2,300 _____.
        (customary)

9b. Lee is measuring the distance from home plate to first base to set up the kickball field. He doesn't have any standard measuring tools so he takes big steps. He took 25 big steps. The distance from home plate to first base is about 25

_____.
        (metric)

❿ Using your centimeter ruler and inch ruler, draw and label the following lengths of lines in the square below.

10 centimeters

Five and one half inches

Topic 3, Subtopic 5 Assessment:
Area and Perimeter

Use the following information to answer questions 1-4.

INTERIOR FLOOR REGION OF FARMER BROWN'S BARN

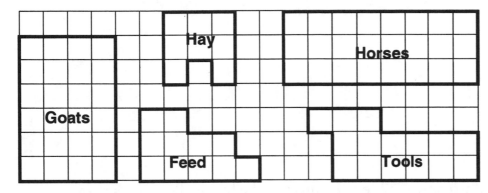

KEY

—— = 1 unit

☐ = 1 square unit

❶ What is the perimeter of the feed section in the barn?

   A. 8 units

   B. 11 units

   C. 16 units

   D. 19 units

❷ Which two regions of Farmer Brown's barn have the same perimeter?

   F. feed and hay

   G. hay and tools

   H. horses and goats

   I. tools and goats

Refer to the diagram on the previous page for questions 3 and 4.

❸ Which two regions of Farmer Brown's barn have the same area?

    A. goats and hay

    B. goats and horses

    C. hay and feed

    D. tools and horses

❹ Farmer Brown needs to put up new wire fencing around the hay section of his barn. How much wire fencing should he purchase?

    F. 14 units

    G. 12 units

    H. 10 units

    I. 8 units

❺ Look at the figure of the rhombus. Which equation could be used to find its perimeter?

rhombus

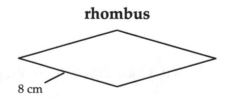

8 cm

    A. $4 \times 8 = p$

    B. $4 \times 4 = p$

    C. $(2 \times 4) + (2 \times 8) = p$

    D. $8 \times 5 = p$

Name: _____

Use the information below to answer questions 6 and 7.

The grid represents Uncle Frank's property.

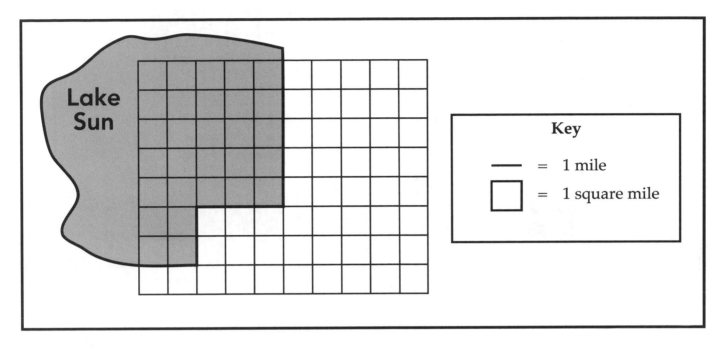

6 Which is the best estimate for the area owned by Uncle Frank that is covered by Lake Sun?

    F. 26 square miles

    G. 29 square miles

    H. 35 square miles

    I. 80 square miles

7 Is this statement true or false?

> About 18 miles of the lake's edge (or shore) are within Uncle Frank's property.

True or false? _____

Explain your thinking. _____

_____

Use the following grid to answers questions 8-10.

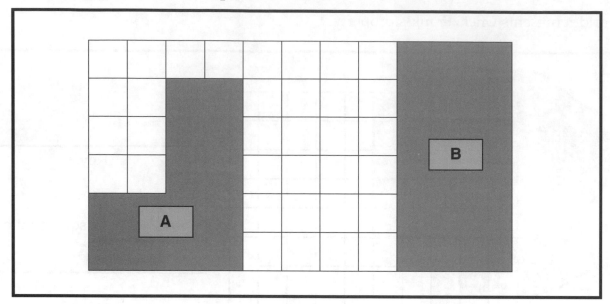

8 Which shaded figure has the greater perimeter? _____

Explain your thinking. _____

_____

9 What is the area of the grid NOT shaded in? _____

Explain your thinking. _____

_____

_____

10 Which is greater, the combined perimeters of the two shaded regions or the perimeter

of the entire grid? _____

Explain your thinking. _____

_____

_____

Topic 3, Subtopic 6 Assessment:
Capacity, Temperature, Weight, and Mass

❶ Which unit would be the best to measure the amount of water in a large cooler?

A. gram   C. liter

B. kilogram   D. milliliter

❷ About how much water could you hold in the palm of your hand?

F. a quart   H. an ounce

G. a pint   I. a gallon

❸ Which unit should you use when measuring the mass of a doughnut?

A. grams   C. liters

B. kilograms   D. meters

4   Mickey says his horse weighs 1,200. He didn't say the unit for the weight. Which standard unit should follow the 1,200 Mickey stated?

     F. tons

     G. pounds

     H. ounces

     I. gallons

5   Use the balance below to answer this question.

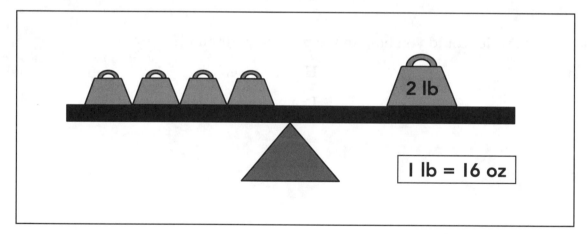

The balance is even. What is the value of each weight on the left side of the balance?

     A. 2 ounces

     B. 4 ounces

     C. 6 ounces

     D. 8 ounces

Name: _____

6 Scott was mowing the lawn on a sunny summer day in Key West, Florida. He looked at his Celsius thermometer to determine exactly how hot it was outside. Which thermometer below did he most likely see?

Circle the letter of the correct thermometer.

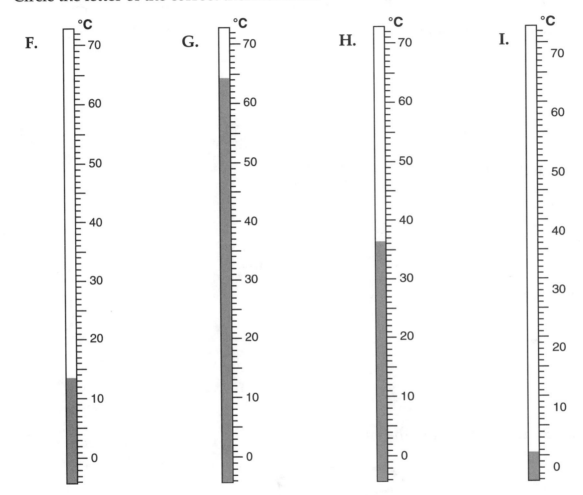

7 For a math measurement assignment, Nancy had to measure the distance from her front door to the edge of the street, a distance of about 20 feet. Part of her assignment was that she could not use a standard measuring tool. Is the following statement true or false?

A paper clip would be a good nonstandard tool to measure this distance.

True or false? _____

Explain your thinking. _____

_____

8 For each item below, circle the best estimate of the temperature in degrees Fahrenheit.

    8a. a cup of hot soup just out of the microwave   80°F   140°F

    8b. your body temperature right now   130°F   98°F

    8c. a pot of boiling water   165°F   212°F

9 Match the unit to the situation.

    Capacity   Grams

    Weight   Pints

    Mass   Celsius

    Temperature   Tons

10 There are 50 liters of water in the tank.

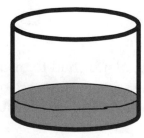

    About how many liters of water will the tank hold when it is full? _____

    Explain your thinking. _____

_____

Topic 4, Subtopic 1 Assessment:
Multiplication Concepts and Facts

---

❶   Which equation is true?

     A. $4 \times 5 = 5 + 4$ **C.** $5 \times 4 = 4 + 5 + 4 + 5$

     B. $4 \times 5 = 5 + 5 + 5 + 5$ **D.** $5 \times 4 = 4 + 4 + 4 + 4$

❷   Which expression best represents the picture?

     F. $6 + 4$ **H.** 4×4

     G. $6 + 4 + 6 + 4$ **I.** 4×6

❸   Which array represents **6 x 5**?

     A.   **C.**

   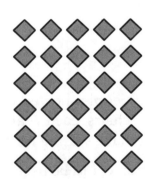

     B.   **D.**

---

4 The commuter train picks up 8 passengers at each of the first 4 stops. During the rest of the train's journey, another 60 passengers get on. How many passengers got on at the first four stops?

F. 4

G. 12

H. 32

I. 92

5 Nick's dad worked eight hours a day, Monday through Friday, at the airport. Nick wants to know how many hours his dad worked during the entire week. What should Nick predict about the solution?

A. It will be greater than 8.

B. It will be between 8 and 5.

C. It will be between 8 and 4.

D. It will be less than 8.

6 One hundred people showed up for the concert in the park. There were 9 rows with 8 chairs, each available for seating. How many more chairs (c) are needed to have seating for all 100 people?

Which equation could be used to solve the problem?

F. $9 + 8 + 100 = c$

G. $9 \times 8 + c = 100$

H. $98 + c = 100$

I. $100 - 9 + 8 = c$

Name: _____

❼ Is the following statement true or false?

The expression 6 x 8 has the same value as the expression 8 x 6.

True or false? _____

Explain your thinking. _____

_____

❽ Draw a picture that represents the following number sentence.

8 x 4 = 32

Use the information to answer questions 9 and 10.

Bob owns a shop that specializes in very unique bicycles, tricycles, and other pedal-powered transportation. He has designed some vehicles that have 4, 5, and even 6 wheels.

BOB'S BIZARRE BIKES, TRIKES, AND BEYOND

Vehicles	Number of Wheels	Price Range
Bicycles	2	$15 - $300
Tricycles	3	$25 - $230
Bicycles with sidecar	3	$185 - $275
Quadra Cycle	4	$140 - $420
Penta Cycle	5	$220 - $300
Hexa Cycle	6	$325 - $545

9 Bob needs to order wheels for 9 Quadra Cycles that he is building.

What is the minimum number of wheels he will need to order? _____

Explain your thinking. _____

_____

10 Bob has the following vehicles on the showroom floor: 5 tricycles, 4 Penta Cycles, 6 Hexa Cycles, and 8 bicycles with sidecars.

How many wheels are on the showroom floor? _____

Show your work in the space below.

Topic 4, Subtopic 2 Assessment:
Division Concepts and Facts

❶ Which equation is missing from the fact family?

| $3 \times 8 = 24$ | $24 \div 3 = 8$ | $8 \times 3 = 24$ |

A. $24 \div 8 = 3$ **C.** $24 - 8 = 16$

B. $24 + 3 = 27$ **D.** $8 \div 24 = 0.33$

❷ Which model could be used to solve the problem?

Yesterday, eighteen people sailed to an island on three sailboats. The same number of people boarded each boat. It took thirty minutes for each boat to sail out to the island. How many people boarded each sailboat before leaving for the island?

F.
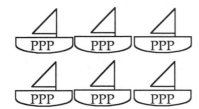

H.
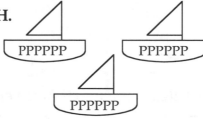

G.

I.
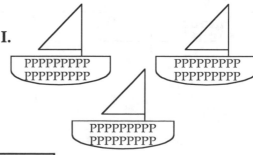

```
           KEY
      P = one person
```

❸ The equation $35 \div 7 = p$ could be used to solve which of the following scenarios?

   A. Thirty-five cars and seven buses are parked. How many vehicles are parked (p)?

   B. Thirty-five beans are split into piles of seven. How many piles (p) are there?

   C. Thirty-five pigs are eating; seven are not. How many pigs (p) are there in all?

   D. Thirty-five bags each hold seven pennies. How many pennies (p) are there combined?

❹ During the early morning, 50 tourists wait for the vans that will take them to Sea World. Each van holds 9 passengers. Six vans arrive and the tourists board the vans. How many seats are empty?

   F. 0 seats

   G. 4 seats

   H. 5 seats

   I. 41 seats

❺ What is the rule for the function table?

Input (n)	63	56	49	42	35	28
Output	9	8	7	6	5	4

   A. $n \times 7$

   B. $n \div 10$

   C. $n - 54$

   D. $n \div 7$

❻ Tricia is cutting string to make bracelets. She has 45 inches of string. She cuts the string into 7-inch pieces. What is the greatest number of bracelets she can make? How long is the leftover piece?

    F. 8 bracelets; 11 inches left over   **H.** 6 bracelets; 3 inches left over

    G. 7 bracelets; 4 inches left over   **I.** 5 bracelets; 10 inches left over

❼ Is the following statement true or false?

This is a fact family.	7×6	6×7	$49 \div 7$	$49 \div 6$

True or false? _____

Explain your thinking. _____

_____

❽ Ring groups of cans in the array to show $36 \div 9 = 4$.

9 Wilson works at the "Set of Four Pack-it Store." All the boxes they use will only hold four items each. A customer orders 35 items.

How many boxes will Wilson use? _____

The solution to the story problem above has a remainder. What does the remainder

mean? _____

Explain your thinking. _____

_____

_____

10 Fill in the blanks with division expressions to make each equality or inequality true.

10a. $42 \div 7$ =   _____

10b.   _____   > $72 \div 9$

10c.   _____   < $18 \div 6$

Topic 4, Subtopic 3 Assessment:
Multiplying Whole Numbers

1 The Customer Comes First rental car company gave each of their 47 customers a six-dollar coupon for a local restaurant. What is the best estimate for the total value of the coupons?

    A. $100

    B. $200

    C. $300

    D. $400

2 Two planes are loaded with cargo. The first plane is loaded with seven containers, each weighing 362 kilograms. The second plane is loaded with three containers, each weighing 719 kilograms. How many kilograms of cargo are being loaded onto the first plane?

    F. 4,691 kg

    G. 2,534 kg

    H. 2,157 kg

    I. 1,081 kg

3 Nine hundred cars drove through the tollbooth during a 5-hour period. On average, how many cars (c) drove through each hour?

Which number sentence could be used to find the solution to the problem?

    A. $5 + 900 = c$

    B. $5 \times c = 900$

    C. $900 \times c = 5$

    D. $900 \times 5 = c$

Use the following information to answer questions 4 and 5.

MEASUREMENT TOOLS ORDER FORM

Item	Cost per item	Number of items ordered	Total cost
Ruler (24-pack)	$3	35	?
Trundle Wheel	$9	175	?
Balance	$7	62	?
Thermometer	$2	284	?

4 What is the total cost for the order of balances?

F. $69   H. $424

G. $139   I. $434

5 How much greater is the cost for the order of trundle wheels than the order of thermometers?

A. $467   C. $1,033

B. $1,007   D. $1,143

6 Tread on Me Sod Farms laid grass in a median located between two streets. They covered the entire median with about 2,000 square feet of sod.

About 2,000 square feet

Which dimensions best describe the size of the median?

F. 3 ft by 200 ft   G. 5 ft by 250 ft   H. 7 ft by 430 ft   I. 9 ft by 220 ft

Name: _____

Use the following information to answer questions 7 and 8.

The Sports Card Emporium sells boxes of mixed trading cards in a variety of sizes.

SPORTS CARD EMPORIUM MIXED TRADING CARDS PRICE LIST

Name of Box	Just For Me	Let's Share	Trading Party	Super Sampler
Number of Cards	30 cards per box	85 cards per box	175 cards per box	350 cards per box
Price	$2.00	$4.00	$6.00	$10.00

7 Is the following statement true or false?

> Buying four boxes of "Let's Share" Trading Cards gives more cards than buying one box of "Super Sampler."

True or false? _____

Explain your thinking. _____

_____

8 Kyle bought 28 of the "Just For M" boxes. Keenan bought 14 of the "Let's Share" boxes. Is the following statement true or false?

> Kyle spent the same amount as Keenan.

True or false? _____

Explain your thinking. _____

_____

9 There are seven conference rooms in a large hotel. Each room can hold a maximum of 524 people. During a busy night, all of the conference rooms will be used. The hotel manager predicts that each will be occupied nearly to the maximum capacity.

About how many people is the manager expecting? _____

Explain your thinking. _____

_____

10 The average person takes about 30,000 breaths in a 24-hour period. About how many times does the average person take a breath in a week?

Would you expect the solution to this problem to be in the hundreds, thousands,

ten thousands, hundred thousands, or millions? _____

Explain your thinking. _____

_____

Topic 4, Subtopic 4 Assessment:
Multiplying Greater Numbers

1 John is turning his garage into a third bedroom. He is trying to figure out about how many square feet of tile he needs to buy for the new room. He measures the floor and estimates that he needs 400 square feet of tile.

24 feet

21 feet

What do you know about John's estimate?

A. The estimate is less than the exact number of square feet.

B. The estimate is greater than the exact number of square feet.

C. The estimate and the exact number of square feet are the same.

D. None of the above.

Use the information and the chart to answer questions 2 and 3.

Dale works part-time at a local department store. He knows how many hours he is going to work each week in February. He wants to figure out how much money he will get each week. Dale earns the same amount every hour that he works.

Dale's February Income

Week	Hours per Week	Income
1	10	$140.00
2	12	
3	14	
4	16	

2 How much will Dale earn Week 3?

F. $42.00   **G.** $140.00   **H.** $196.00   **I.** not enough information to answer the question

3 How much will Dale earn in February?

A. $168.00   **B.** $224.00   **C.** $588.00   **D.** $728.00

Use the following graph to answer question 4 and 5.

Trees in Four City Parks

Name of Park	Approximate Number of trees
Foliage Park	🌳 🌳 🌳 🌳 🌳
Green Day Park	🌳 🌳 🌳 🌳 🌳 🌳
Dewy Leaf Park	🌳 🌳 🌳
Shady Place Park	🌳 🌳 🌳 🌳 🌳

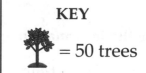

KEY

🌳 = 50 trees

❹ About how many trees are in all four of the city parks?

    F. 19

    G. 135

    H. 190

    I. 950

❺ If the key showed that one tree symbol stood for 75 trees, how about many trees would be in the four parks?

    A. 75

    B. 150

    C. 1,425

    D. 3,750

Name: _____

Use the function table for questions 6 and 7.

6 The rule for the table is $10n$.

Input (n):	2	20	200	2,000	20,000	200,000
Output:	20	200	2,000	20,000		A

What number replaces **A**?

   F. 20,000   **G.** 200,000   **H.** 2,000,000   **I.** 20,000,000

7 Examine the function table to see what generalization you can make about multiplying by 10. Use that information to decide whether the following statement is true or false.

> The number 9,654 multiplied by 10 is 965,400.

True or false? _____

Explain your thinking. _____

_____

8 Elizabeth wanted to know how much a trip ticket to Washington, D.C., would cost for the twelve winners of the spelling bee. She found out that the trip would cost $255 per person. To find the total amount of money, Elizabeth wrote the problem this way:

> $255 x 12 = ($255 x 10) + ($255 x 2)

What property of multiplication was Elizabeth using? _____

Explain your answer. _____

_____

9 Ms. Robinson's class decided to try to earn money for a class trip. They had three bake sales and made $360. They used all of that money to start their own book fair. They bought used children's books for $1.00 each. They sold each book for $5.00.

How much money did they make in all? _____

Show your work, telling what steps you used to solve the problem.

10 Study the function table.

Input (n)	Output
9	108
18	216
27	324
36	
54	

What is the rule for the function table? _____

Complete the function table, using the rule.

How do you know the rule? _____

_____

_____

Topic 4, Subtopic 5 Assessment:
Adding and Subtracting Decimals

❶ Beth went to the school store and spent $4.89 on school supplies. If Beth paid the store clerk with a ten-dollar bill, how much change will she receive?

    A. $3.89

    B. $4.11

    C. $5.11

    D. $6.89

❷ Lovell bought a drink for $1.39 and a super salad for $4.92. His friend Julius bought a value meal for $5.65. How much more did Lovell spend on his meal than Julius spent on his?

    F. $11.96

    G. $6.31

    H. $0.66

    I. $0.34

❸ The *humerus* is the bone in your upper arm. In an adult man, the average length of this bone is 14.35 inches. The *femur* is the bone in your upper leg. In an adult man, the average length of this bone is 19.88 inches. How much longer is the femur than the humerus in an average adult man?

    A. 4.53 inches

    B. 5.53 inches

    C. 5.63 inches

    D. 34.23 inches

Use the following information to answer questions 4 and 5.

At the science center is a habitat featuring some of the world's smallest mammals. The informational flyer shows the average weights and lengths of the animals in the habitat.

A Look at Some Really Small Mammals!!!		
Name	Length (in inches)	Weight (in ounces)
Harvest mouse	2.3 in.	0.19 oz
Little brown bat	1.6 in.	0.28 oz
Pygmy shrew	1.4 in.	0.05 oz
Water shrew	2.8 in.	0.41 oz

4 How much more does the heaviest mammal in the habitat weigh than the lightest mammal?

F. 0.22 oz

G. 0.36 oz

H. 44 oz

I. 46 oz

5 The habitat caretaker put one of each type mammal together on a digital scale. Each one was very close to the average weights shown on the informational flyer. Which scale most likely held the four animals altogether?

A.

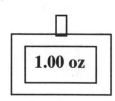

1.00 oz

B.

0.50 oz

C.

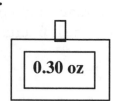

0.30 oz

D.

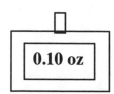

0.10 oz

Name: _____

6 At the "It Fits Jewelry Store," you can buy a gold chain cut to any metric length. Cheyenne bought 0.81 meter to make her own bracelets. Fernando bought 0.39 meter for a necklace. Ursula bought 0.24 meter for an anklet. How much more was purchased by Cheyenne than purchased by Ursula and Fernando combined?

    F. 1.8 meters

    G. 0.81 meter

    H. 0.28 meter

    I. 0.18 meter

7 Is the following statement true or false?

The combined mass of 0.67 gram and 0.37 gram is more than a gram.

True or false? _____

Explain your thinking. _____

_____

Use the graph to answer questions 8-10.

Troy was doing an experiment. He wanted to find out how much dew collects around his house overnight. He also wanted to know if the amount of dew is affected by location. He measured the dew on four different mornings. He used two locations: in the front yard of his house and underneath a bush in his backyard.

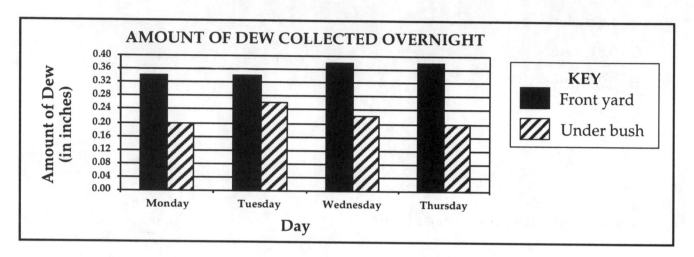

❽ On what day was the difference in the amount of dew collected at the two locations 0.16 inch? _____

    Explain your thinking. _____

_____

❾ What was the total amount of dew collected at the two locations on Tuesday? _____
Show your work.

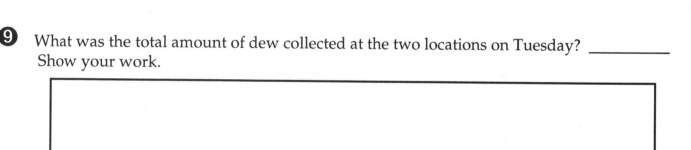

❿ Use a calculator to find the mean amount of dew collected at each location. Compare the two mean amounts. Then, write a comparison statement.

_____

_____

Topic 4, Subtopic 6 Assessment:
Dividing Greater Numbers

❶ In a city basketball league, six players tied for high points on Saturday. The number of points scored by all six players combined was 96. How many points did each player score on Saturday?

    A. 11 points

    B. 16 points

    C. 24 points

    D. 368 points

❷ Three friends decided to equally share the cost of a go-cart. The go-cart cost $610. About how much did each friend have to spend to buy the go-cart?

    F. About $200

    G. About $400

    H. About $600

    I. About $1800

❸ Walter has 344 coins. He sorts his coins into pennies, nickels, dimes, and quarters. To his amazement, he has the same number of each type of coin. How many coins worth more than five cents does Walter have?

    A. 35

    B. 86

    C. 172

    D. 344

4 The picture below represents a display table in the Hall of Fame that holds baseballs signed by famous players. The combined weight of the signed balls on the table is 850 grams(g). How much does one ball weigh?

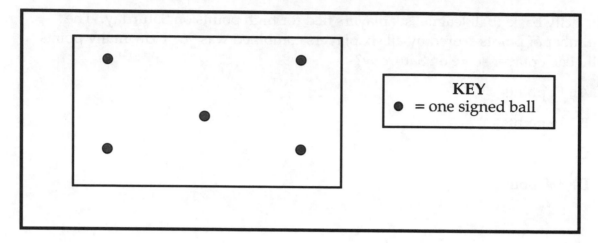

F. 170 g

G. 180 g

H. 190 g

I. 200 g

5 Gerry has 267 photographs that he wants to put in an album. He decides to put 8 on a page and keep the leftover photographs out of the album until he develops more pictures and can fill another page. How many photographs will Gerry have to save until he has more pictures?

A. 8

B. 6

C. 4

D. 3

Name: _____

Use the information and data tables to answer questions 6-8.

The Wilderness Rescue Organization holds a yearly search and rescue competition. The prize money is split up evenly among the team members. The results of the competition are presented below.

DIVISION ONE (5-PERSON TEAM)		
Place	Team	Prize $ for Team
1st	Rockhoppers	650
2nd	Trailblazers	335
3rd	Path Patrol	165

DIVISION TWO (7-PERSON TEAM)		
Place	Team	Prize $ for Team
1st	Giving It All	875
2nd	Tough Troop	420
3rd	Gogetters	210

6 How much did each individual receive who was on the second place team in Division One?

F. $650   G. $167   H. $85   I. $67

7 Is the following statement true or false?

> Each team member from the "Giving It All" team received more than $120.

True or false? _____

Explain your thinking. _____

_____

8 On one team, every member earned exactly half as much as each member of the team that finished one place ahead of them. Which team is that?

Answer: _____

Explain your thinking. _____

_____

9 Joe has a deck of 52 cards. After he deals out 7 cards to each player in the game, there are 10 cards left in the deck.

How many players are in the game? _____

Explain your thinking. _____

_____

10 Write an equation using the variable *t* that could be used to solve the story problem.

There are 387 trophies evenly distributed into nine boxes for delivery to six different stores. How many trophies(*t*) are in each box?

10a. Equation: _____

10b. Show your work.

10c. The number of trophies: _____

Topic 5, Subtopic 1 Assessment:
Relating Area and Perimeter

Use this grid map of a few blocks in Central City to answer questions 1-4.

The shaded areas represent each store's property. Each section separated by streets is a city block.

KEY

—— = 1 unit   ☐ = 1 square unit

❶ Central City Self-Storage is putting a security fence around their property. How many units of fencing will they need to enclose their property?

    A. 12 units   **B.** 15 units   **C.** 20 units   **D.** 24 units

❷ The Center of Gravity Science Shop is thinking about buying all the remaining square units available on their block. How many square units will the science shop own if they expand their store to include the remaining square units?

    F. 24 square units   **G.** 20 square units   **H.** 17 square units   **I.** 7 square units

❸ Middle Valley Movies and The Core Café are going to combine their properties. They will buy the square unit marked with the "**X**" to connect their stores. What will be the combined area of their new property including the piece they bought?

    A. 6 square units   **B.** 11 square units   **C.** 18 square units   **D.** 22 square units

4 Use the grid map on the previous page to answer this question. A survey crew was hired to find each property's perimeter (length of property line). How much greater in length is Center Point Cycles' property line than Epicenter Entertainment's property line?

F. 2 units   G. 8 units   H. 14 units   I. 22 units

Use the information and drawing of the island to answer questions 5 and 6.

The total coastline of Fog Island is 225 miles. Each point along the coastline is a distance marker. The distance between each marker is labeled except for one portion of the coastline.

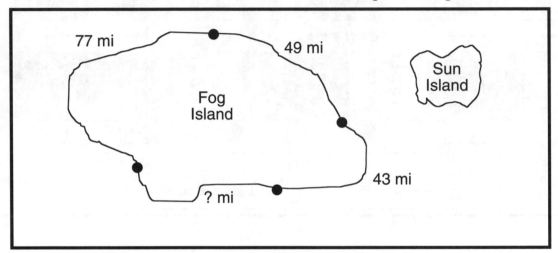

5 How long is the unmarked distance of the coastline?

A. 56 miles   C. About 90 miles

B. 89 miles   D. Impossible to determine

6 Sun Island has about 500 square miles of land area. Which is the best estimate for the square mileage of Fog Island?

F. About 500 square miles   H. About 5,000 square miles

G. About 1000 square miles   I. About 10,000 square miles

Name: _____

❼ Use the grid to answer the question.

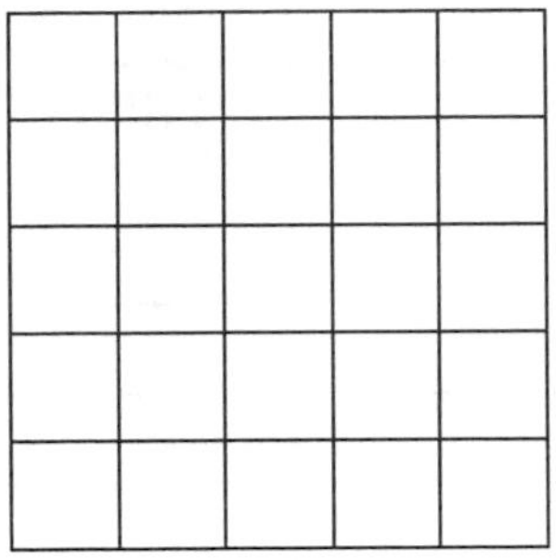

KEY

—— = 1 unit

☐ = 1 square unit

Is the following statement true or false?

Adding one row of square units to the grid would double the perimeter of the figure.

True or false? _____

Explain your thinking. _____

_____

❽ You have 24 yards of decorative border stone to go around the edge of a new garden that you are planning. Draw your plan for a garden on the grid below so that it has a perimeter of 24 yards. You want to create an interesting shape, so the shape of your garden *cannot* be a rectangle.

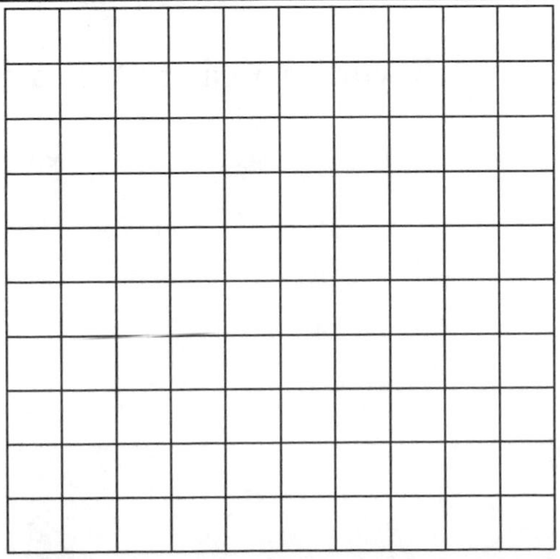

KEY

☐ = 1 square yard

—— = 1 yard

Use the grids to answer questions 9 and 10.

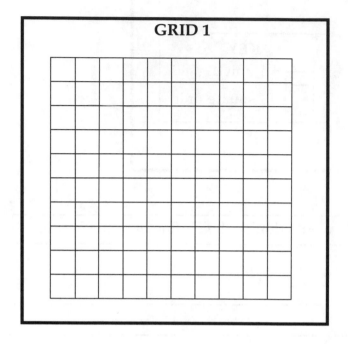

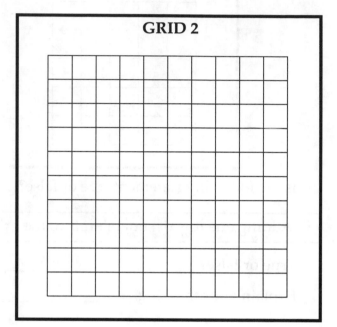

9 On GRID 1, draw two rectangles that have the same perimeter.

The two rectangles can NOT be congruent. Label the dimensions.

10 On GRID 2, draw two congruent figures, each with an area of 13 square units.

Topic 5, Subtopic 2 Assessment:
Solid Figures and Volume

❶ Which of the following figures has only triangular faces?

    A. cube

    B. square pyramid

    C. triangular prism

    D. triangular pyramid

❷ Which 2-dimensional net could be folded to make a cube?

F.

H.

G.

I.

Use the following key to answer questions 3-5.

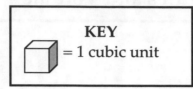

KEY

= 1 cubic unit

❸ How many cubic units are in the rectangular prism shown?

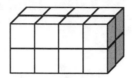

A. 8 B. 16 C. 20 D. 32

❹ Marvin must create two equal groups using the cubic units below. How many cubic units will be in each group?

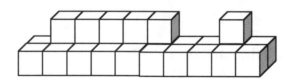

F. 10 G. 13 H. 20 I. 26

❺ At Josie's furniture store they sell chairs made up of big foam cubes. Customers design their own chairs and the store covers them with material. The surfaces that you cannot see from this viewpoint are flat. Which chair below has a volume of 24 cubic units?

A. 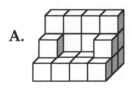 B. 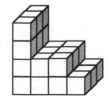 C. 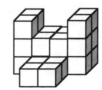 D.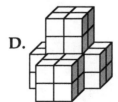

Name: _____

6 Use the table and drawings to answer the question.

Faces	Vertices	Edges
5	5	8

Which figure below fits the attributes listed in the table?

F.

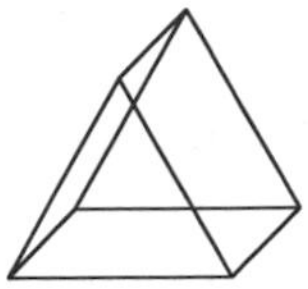

Triangular Prism

G.

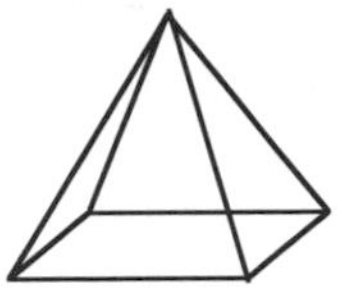

Square Pyramid

H.

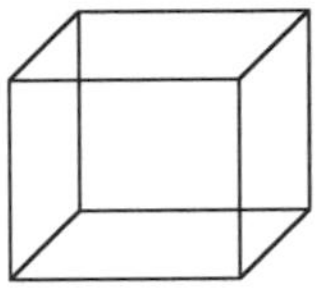

Rectangular Prism

I.

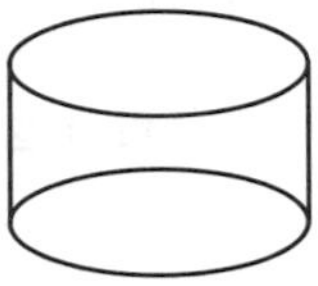

Cylinder

7 Is the following statement true or false?

A triangular prism has the same number of faces as a square pyramid.

True or false? _____

Explain your thinking. _____

_____

8 The following pictures represent a top view and two different side views of a rectangular prism.

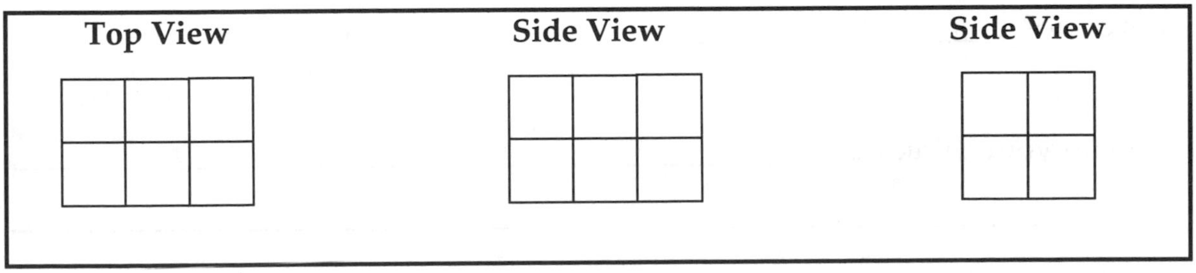

Top View	Side View	Side View

What is the volume of the rectangular prism?_____

Explain your thinking. _____

_____

❾ Fill in the attribute table for the figures listed.

Name of Figure	Faces	Picture	Vertices	Edges
Cylinder			0	
Triangular Prism				9
Square Pyramid	5			

❿ Using ALL of the cubic units below, could you create one larger cube?

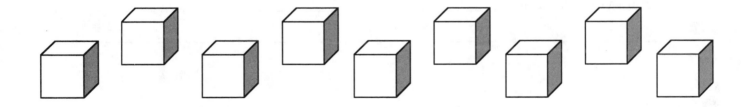

Yes or no? _____

Explain your thinking. _____

_____

Topic 5, Subtopic 3 Assessment:
Time

---

1 Lysette did her math and science homework before going to bed. Which is the best estimate for the amount of time she spent on her math and science homework?

    A. 40 seconds   **C.** 4 days

    B. 40 minutes   **D.** 4 years

2 What is one way to say the time shown on the clock?

    F. quarter past four   **H.** quarter past five

    G. quarter to four   **I.** quarter to five

3 Jordan went on a deep sea fishing trip. The fishing boat left the docks at 6:35 A.M. The boat returned 11 hours later. When did the boat return to the docks?

    A. 7:35 P.M.   **C.** 5:35 P.M.

    B. 6:35 P.M.   **D.** 4:35 P.M.

4 Stocky Jones works at a grocery store. The grocery store closes at 9:00 P.M. Stocky left 22 minutes before the store closed. What is the best estimate for the time Stocky left the grocery store?

F. quarter to nine   H. eight o'clock

G. quarter past nine   I. nine o'clock

Use the table to answer questions 5 and 6.

Equivalent Measures of Time
1 year = 12 months = 365 days
1 decade = 10 years
1 century = 100 years
1 millennium = 1,000 years

5 Gregory bought a car. He has to make payments on it for the next 60 months. For how many years will Gregory make payments on the car?

A. 60 years   C. 5 years

B. 12 years   D. 2 years

6 Believe it or not, chewing gum was invented in 1875 and the ice cream cone was invented in 1904. About how many decades passed between the invention of each item?

F. about 3 decades   H. about 7 decades

G. about 15 decades   I. about 25 decades

Name: _____

Use the calendar to answer questions 7 and 8.

May						
Sun.	Mon.	Tues.	Wed.	Thurs.	Fri.	Sat.
				1	2	3
4	5	6	7	8	9	10
11	12	13	14	15	16	17
18	19	20	21	22	23	24
25	26	27	28	29	30	31

7 Beginning in May, Christopher has soccer practice every Tuesday and Thursday. Is the following statement true or false?

> Christopher will attend the sixth soccer practice for the month of May on May 22.

True or false? _____

Explain your thinking. _____

_____

8 Benjamin received a science kit on the 29th. He ordered the science kit on the 14th of May. How long, from the day Benjamin ordered the science kit, did it take for the kit to arrive at Benjamin's house?

Answer: _____

Explain your thinking. _____

_____

9 Is the following statement true or false?

> The time "twenty-five minutes before eight o'clock" is 7:25.

True or false? _____

Explain your thinking. _____

_____

10 Shaniqua decides to go to the grocery store to buy items for dinner. She leaves her house at 12:45 P.M. The shopping trip took three quarters of an hour. Show the time Shaniqua arrived home by drawing the hands on the clock below. Explain why you drew the hour hand in the location that you did.

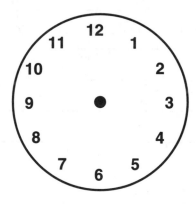

_____

_____

_____

Topic 5, Subtopic 4 Assessment:
Using Measures

❶ You are going to build a dog kennel in your back yard. You need 19 feet of fencing to construct this kennel. The store sells fencing only by the yard. What is the least amount of fencing you will need to buy?

> 12 inches = 1 foot
>
> 3 feet = 1 yard

   A. 3 yards   **B.** 6 yards   **C.** 7 yards   **D.** 9 yards

❷ At the killer whale exhibit, the sign read, "Bashful, our largest killer whale, weighs in at an astounding six _____!" What unit of measure would best fit in the blank?

   F. grams   **G.** meters   **H.** pounds   **I.** tons

❸ Use your centimeter ruler for this question. How much greater is the perimeter of the rectangle than the perimeter of the trapezoid?

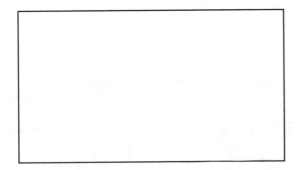
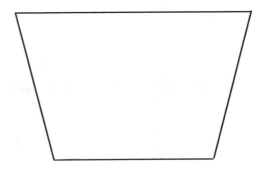

   A. 4 cm   **C.** 18 cm

   B. about 16 cm   **D.** about 20 cm

4 Which roof peak (top) most likely has an angle greater than 90°?

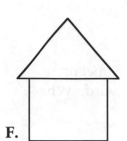 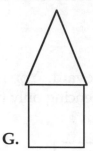 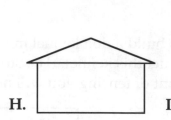 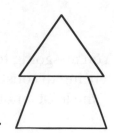

F.   G.   H.   I.

5 Hans stepped outside in a pair of shorts and a short-sleeved shirt. He found it a bit chilly. He decided to put on long pants and a light jacket. Which thermometer is the best example for the temperature when Hans walked outside?

A. 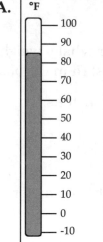   B. 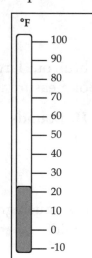   C. 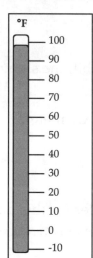   D.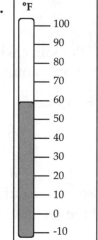

6 The tub below will hold 12 gallons. How many quarts will the tub hold?

2 pints = 1 quart
4 quarts = 1 gallon

F. 36   G. 48   H. 60   I. 72

Name: _____

❼ Use an inch ruler to answer the question. Is the following statement true or false?

> The arrow below is about 4 and a half inches in length.

$$\longrightarrow$$

True or false? _____

Explain your thinking. _____

_____

❽ Complete the following T-Chart and then answer the question below.

Meters (m)	Kilometers (km)
1,000	1.0
1,500	1.5
2,000	2.0
2,500	2.5
3,000	3.0
3,500	3.5
4,000	
4,500	
5,000	

$$1,000 \text{ m} = 1 \text{ km}$$

How many meters are in 7.5 kilometers? _____

Explain your thinking. _____

_____

9 Match the scenario to the unit that it best fits. The first one is done for you.

years	grams	cubic inches
miles	meters	square yards
gallons	degrees	milliliters

Distance across the United States   *miles*

Mass of a potato chip   _____

Height of a 10-story building   _____

Capacity of a drinking glass   _____

Volume of a solid block of wood   _____

Area of a playground   _____

10 The pattern below continues. What is the perimeter of the 5th rectangle?

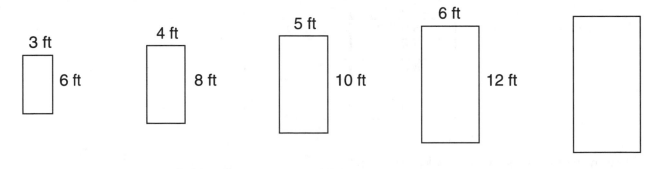

3 ft   6 ft   4 ft   8 ft   5 ft   10 ft   6 ft   12 ft

Answer: _____

Explain your thinking. _____

_____

Topic 6, Subtopic 1 Assessment:
Fraction Concepts

❶ What fractional part of the sports figures are tennis players?

A. $\frac{4}{4}$ B. $\frac{3}{4}$ C. $\frac{1}{3}$ D. $\frac{1}{4}$

Use the following information to answer questions 2 and 3.

Five groups of students are making flags to represent their field day teams.
Each flag is the same size. Their rough draft designs are shown below.

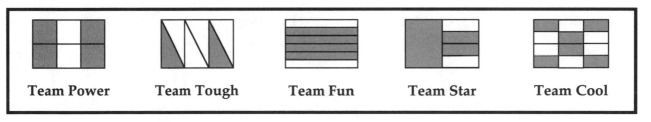

Team Power   **Team Tough**   **Team Fun**   **Team Star**   **Team Cool**

❷ Which two teams' flags show equivalent parts shaded in?

   F. Team Tough and Team Star   H. Team Power and Team Fun

   G. Team Star and Team Cool   I. Team Cool and Team Tough

❸ Which team's flag is $\frac{1}{3}$ shaded?

   A. Team Cool   B. Team Fun   C. Team Power   D. Team Tough

Use the following information to answer questions 4-6.

Ellen lives in Sebring, FL. She has some friends that live in other Florida cities. They are all interested in weather. They each have a rain gauge on their house. They record the amount of rain at the end of each week and then share their results in the table below.

Name	Week 1	Week 2	Week 3
Dustin	$\frac{3}{16}$ inch	$\frac{3}{4}$ inch	$\frac{1}{8}$ inch
Ellen	$\frac{3}{8}$ inch	$\frac{1}{3}$ inch	$\frac{1}{4}$ inch
Marcell	$1\frac{1}{2}$ inch	$1\frac{5}{8}$ inch	$1\frac{3}{8}$ inch
Sadie	$\frac{2}{3}$ inch	$\frac{7}{16}$ inch	$\frac{1}{2}$ inch

④ In week 2, who recorded an amount of rainfall closest to 1 inch?

    F. Sadie   **G.** Marcell   **H.** Ellen   **I.** Dustin

⑤ Which person recorded the least rainfall for week 1?

    A. Dustin   **B.** Ellen   **C.** Marcell   **D.** Sadie

⑥ Which shows the rainfall that Marcell recorded listed **least** to **greatest**?

    F. $1\frac{1}{2}, 1\frac{5}{8}, 1\frac{3}{8}$ **H.** $1\frac{3}{8}, 1\frac{5}{8}, 1\frac{1}{2}$

    G. $1\frac{3}{8}, 1\frac{1}{2}, 1\frac{5}{8}$ **I.** $1\frac{5}{8}, 1\frac{3}{8}, 1\frac{1}{2}$

Name: _____

7 At the "It Fits Jewelry Store," customers can buy gold chains of any length. Some customers ask for lengths in inches, some in feet, and some in yards. Here are the lengths of the gold chains purchased by 4 customers.

A. Alfred: 1.75 feet	**C.** Catherine: 18 inches
B. Bettina: $2\frac{1}{2}$ feet	**D.** David: 1 yard

Look at the number lines below. The unit of measure is feet. The letters *A, B, C,* and *D* stand for the length of chain purchased by each of the four customers. Is this statement true or false?

> **Number line F** is the only number line that shows the correct lengths of the chains purchased by the four customers.

True or false? _____

Explain your answer. _____

_____

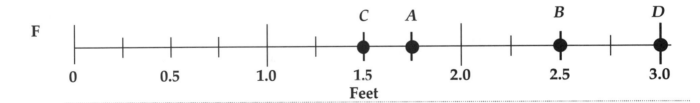

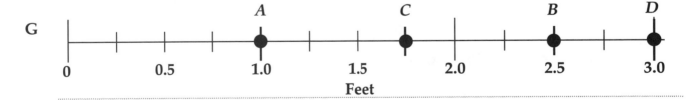

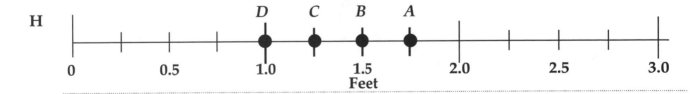

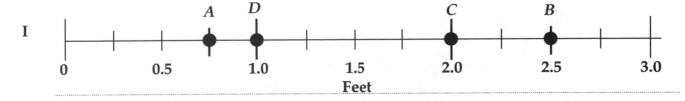

8 Yolanda had four packages of yogurt in her refrigerator. Each package held six containers of yogurt. She ate two and one third of the packages of yogurt during the week. Show this amount by shading in the model below.

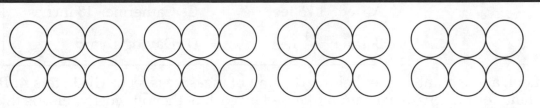

9 Draw a picture to represent each of the fractions listed.

$\dfrac{5}{8}$

seven tenths

$\dfrac{3}{12}$

10 Look at the inequality below.

$\dfrac{6}{8} > n$

Write two fractions that the variable n could represent.

$n = $ _____ , _____

Explain your thinking. _____

_____

Topic 6, Subtopic 2 Assessment:
Adding and Subtracting Fractions and Mixed Numbers

1 Maurice Rapido is preparing for an upcoming sprint race. He sprints $\frac{3}{10}$ mile every time he practices. About how far does Maurice sprint in two practices?

    A. about $\frac{1}{10}$ mile   **C.** about $\frac{9}{10}$ mile

    B. about $\frac{1}{2}$ mile   **D.** about 1 mile

2 Two boats are sailing into port. The boat from Miami has $\frac{7}{8}$ ton of fish. The boat from Ft. Lauderdale has $\frac{3}{8}$ ton of fish. How much more fish is the Miami boat carrying than the Ft. Lauderdale boat?

    F. $\frac{4}{0}$ ton   **H.** $\frac{5}{8}$ ton

    G. $\frac{1}{2}$ ton   **I.** $\frac{10}{8}$ tons

3 Which digit goes in the square to make the number sentence true?

$$\frac{1}{8} + \frac{5}{8} = \frac{\square}{8}$$

    A. 7   **C.** 5

    B. 6   **D.** 4

Use the information below to answer questions 4 and 5.

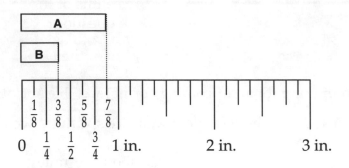

4️⃣ How much longer is strip A than strip B?

F. $\frac{3}{8}$ in.   H. $\frac{3}{4}$ in.

G. $\frac{1}{2}$ in.   I. $\frac{10}{8}$ in.

5️⃣ How long are the two strips combined?

A. $\frac{3}{8}$ in.   C. $\frac{4}{6}$ in.

B. $\frac{6}{12}$ in.   D. $1\frac{1}{4}$ in.

Name: _____

6 Janelle was working on tiling a floor. On Saturday she completed seven sixteenths of the sections. On Sunday, she completed nine sixteenths of the sections. Which model could be used to answer the following question?

How many sections did Janelle finish over the two days?

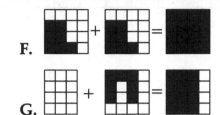

F.

G.

H.

I.

7 Is the following statement true or false?

The difference between $\dfrac{8}{10}$ and $\dfrac{3}{10}$ is $\dfrac{1}{2}$.

True or false? _____

Explain your thinking. _____

_____

8 **8a.** Shade in the model to show the following expression below. Then shade in the answer. Finally, write the answer as a fraction in number form.

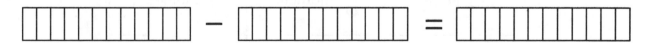

8b. $\dfrac{2}{3}$ $-$ $\dfrac{5}{12}$ $=$ _____

9 On the number line below, show the following equation.

$$4\frac{1}{10} - \frac{3}{5} = \boxed{}$$

3　　　　　　　4　　　　　　　5

Confirm your answer by showing your work here:

10 In a recent contest to navigate on foot through a swampy area in the Everglades, three contestants covered the distances shown in the table.

EVERGLADES CONTEST RESULTS

Contestant	Day 1	Day 2
Nova Scochia	$\frac{3}{5}$ kilometer	$\frac{3}{10}$ kilometer
Jack Farley	$\frac{4}{10}$ kilometer	$\frac{2}{5}$ kilometer
Scott Weber	$\frac{1}{5}$ kilometer	$\frac{1}{2}$ kilometer

contestant with the greatest combined distance on the two days won the competition. Compute the exact distance that each person walked.

Nova Scochia: _____　　　Jack Farley: _____　　　Scott Weber: _____

Topic 6, Subtopic 3 Assessment:
Algebraic Concepts

❶ Which fraction goes in the square to make the number sentence true?

$$\frac{1}{2} + \boxed{} = \frac{5}{8}$$

A. $\frac{5}{4}$ C. $\frac{3}{8}$

B. $\frac{4}{6}$ D. $\frac{1}{8}$

❷ The chart shows the part of each day that two animals spent sleeping.

HOW LONG CAT AND DOG SLEPT

	Day 1	Day 2	Day 3
Cat	$\frac{1}{3}$	$\frac{3}{8}$	$\frac{2}{3}$
Dog	$\frac{1}{4}$	$\frac{6}{8}$	$\frac{1}{2}$

Which equation tells how much longer the cat slept than the dog on day 3?

F. $\frac{1}{3} + \frac{2}{3} = \frac{3}{3}$

G. $\frac{1}{2} + \frac{2}{3} = 1\frac{1}{6}$

H. $\frac{2}{3} - \frac{1}{2} = \frac{1}{6}$

I. $\frac{6}{8} - \frac{3}{8} = \frac{3}{8}$

❸ Twenty-four birds are swimming on a lake. Two thirds of the birds are ducks. One fourth of the birds are geese. The rest of the birds are represented by b.

Which number sentence could be used to represent the information above?

A. $\dfrac{2}{3} - \dfrac{1}{4} + b = \dfrac{24}{24}$

C. $b - \dfrac{2}{3} + \dfrac{1}{4} = \dfrac{24}{24}$

B. $\dfrac{2}{3} + \dfrac{1}{4} + b = \dfrac{24}{24}$

D. $b - \dfrac{2}{3} - \dfrac{1}{4} = \dfrac{24}{24}$

❹ Perry is marking locations on a piece of wood he has to cut. He makes a mark every two and a quarter inches. Which picture shows how he should have marked the piece of wood?

$2\dfrac{1}{4}$ in. $4\dfrac{1}{2}$ in. $6\dfrac{3}{4}$ in. 9 in.

F.

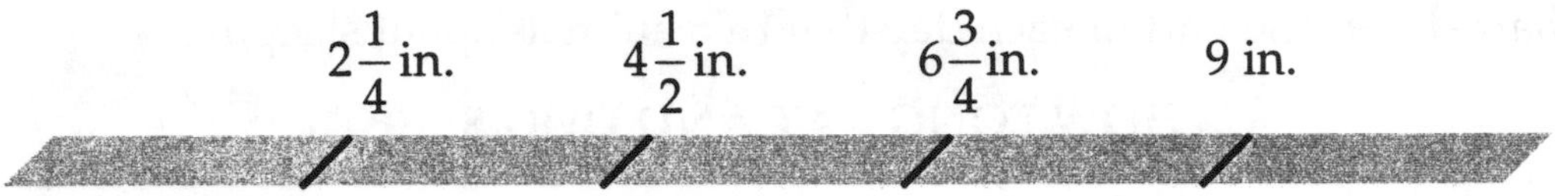

$2\dfrac{1}{4}$ in. $4\dfrac{1}{4}$ in. $6\dfrac{1}{4}$ in. $8\dfrac{1}{4}$ in.

G.

$2\dfrac{1}{4}$ in. $4\dfrac{3}{4}$ in. $7\dfrac{1}{4}$ in. $9\dfrac{3}{4}$ in.

H.

$2\dfrac{1}{4}$ in. $4\dfrac{1}{8}$ in. $6\dfrac{1}{2}$ in. $8\dfrac{1}{8}$ in.

I.

5 Which mixed number can represent the value of *n* in the inequality shown?

$$n + \frac{5}{8} = 3\frac{1}{4}$$

A. $3\frac{1}{4}$ **B.** $3\frac{3}{8}$ **C.** $2\frac{5}{8}$ **D.** $3\frac{1}{2}$

6 What is the rule for the table?

Input (*n*)	Output
5	$2\frac{5}{8}$
7	$4\frac{5}{8}$
9	$6\frac{5}{8}$
11	$8\frac{5}{8}$
13	$10\frac{5}{8}$

F. $n + 2\frac{5}{8}$ **G.** $n - 3\frac{5}{8}$ **H.** $n - 2\frac{3}{8}$ **I.** $n + 2\frac{3}{8}$

7 Is the following statement true or false?

$$\frac{5}{10} + \frac{1}{5} \text{ equals } \frac{1}{2} + \frac{2}{10}$$

True or false? _____

Explain your thinking. _____

_____

8 Write an equation that represents the model. Each shaded piece (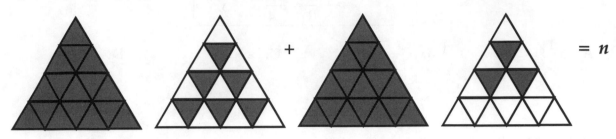) represents an equivalent fractional part.

Equation: _____ + _____ = n

Sum: _____

9 Use a pattern to complete the table.

Cups	10	8	6	4	2
Pints	5	4	3		
Quarts	$2\frac{1}{2}$	2	$1\frac{1}{2}$		

10 Use the completed table from question 9 to answer this question. How many quarts are equal to 14 cups?

Answer: _____

Explain your thinking. _____

_____

Topic 6, Subtopic 4 Assessment:
Multiples, Factors, and Divisibility

❶ Which list of numbers includes all the factors of 32?

    A. 1, 2, 3, 4, 6, 8, 16, 32   **C.** 1, 3, 6, 12, 24, 30

    B. 1, 2, 4, 8, 16, 32   **D.** 0, 4, 8, 12, 16, 20, 24, 28, 32

❷ Antwan is listing the multiples of 4. Pauline is listing the multiples of 7. The first number that both of them list is 28. What is the next number that they will both list?

    F. 35   **H.** 56

    G. 48   **I.** 64

❸ Use the following information to answer the question. The picture below shows a display of paint cans at the hardware store. Rex used five boxes filled with paint cans to make the display. Each box contained the same number of paint cans. When he was done he had two paint cans left over.

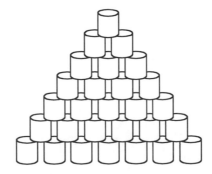

How many paint cans were in each box?

    A. 5   **C.** 7

    B. 6   **D.** 8

Use the following information to answer questions 4 and 5.

Mrs. Kabby is organizing a schedule to take her 3 children to their after-school activities during the month of March. The calendar shows 3 weeks of the schedule that Mrs. Kabby has completed so far.

Mona's activities take place every third day. Ben's activities take place every fourth day. Dee's activities take place every sixth day.

MARCH ACTIVITY CALENDAR

Sunday	Monday	Tuesday	Wednesday	Thursday	Friday	Saturday
1 Ben, Mona	2 Dee	3	4 Mona	5 Ben	6	7 Mona
8 Dee	9 Ben	10 Mona	11	12	13 Ben, Mona	14 Dee
15	16 Mona	17 Ben	18	19 Mona	20 Dee	21 Ben
22	23	24	25	26	27	28
29	30	31				

❹ Complete the March Calendar for Mrs. Kabby. Who has an activity on March 26?

   F. Ben

   G. Dee

   H. Mona

   I. none of the children

❺ On which day of the month will Mrs. Kabby need to take both Mona and Ben to their activities?

   A. March 22

   B. March 25

   C. March 28

   D. March 31

6 How can you tell if a number is divisible by both five and ten?

   F. The last digit in the number is 5.

   G. The last digit in the number is 0.

   H. The first digit in the number is 5.

   I. The first digit in the number is 1.

Use the table to answer questions 7 and 8.

1	4	9	16	___
□	 ⊞	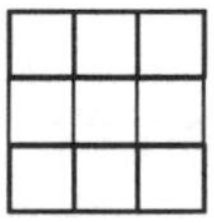 (3×3 grid)	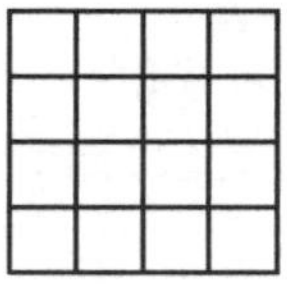 (4×4 grid)	

7 Look at the four models above. Then decide if the following statement is true or false.

> The model that should come next in the table is:
>
> (6×6 grid)

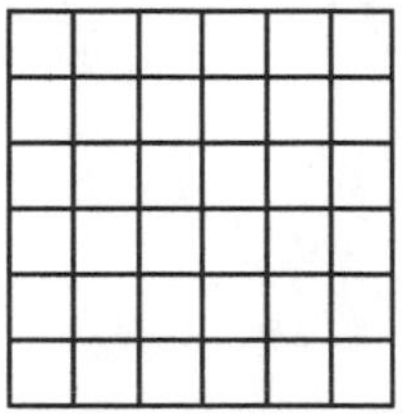

True or false? _____

Explain your thinking. _____

_____

8   **8a.**   Look at the four models (for 1, 4, 9 and 16) in the table on the previous page. Do all of the models represent numbers that have 3 factors? _____

_____

     8b.   Explain your thinking. _____

_____

_____

     8c.   How are all of the models alike? _____

_____

_____

9   I am a number with exactly 6 factors. I am divisible by 2 and 3. The sum of my digits is 9. I am less than 50. Who am I?

     Answer: _____

     Explain your thinking. _____

_____

_____

10   Is 10 a multiple of 3?

     Yes or no? _____

     Explain your thinking. _____

_____

_____

Topic 7, Subtopic 1 Assessment:
Probability

1 Cleo places four white gumballs and one orange gumball into a brown bag. Whoever picks the orange gumball gets to go in the new tree house first. Cleo's sister Ashlyn picks first. Which fraction represents the probability of Ashlyn selecting the orange gumball in the first try?

A. $\dfrac{1}{5}$ C. $\dfrac{4}{5}$

B. $\dfrac{1}{4}$ D. $\dfrac{5}{5}$

2 In the situation from question 1, Ashlyn puts the gumball she drew back in the bag. Her friend Marta then draws a gumball from the bag. What is the likelihood that Marta drew a white gumball?

F. certain   H. likely

G. impossible   I. unlikely

3 How many possible outcomes are there for heads-tails combinations if you randomly toss three coins? Order counts.

Remember: Heads-tails-heads is different from heads-heads-tails.

A. 4   C. 8

B. 6   D. 10

Use the pictures and table below to answer questions 4 and 5.

The table shows all the possible outcomes for the order in which the 4 animal cards could be randomly selected.

F = frog card   **B = bird card**   **H = horse card**   **L = lion card**

FBHL	FBLH	FHBL	FHLB	FLHB	FLBH
BFHL	BFLH	BHLF	BHFL	BLFH	BLHF
HBFL	HBLF	HFBL	HFLB	HLBF	HLFB
LFHB	LFBH	LHFB	LHBF	LBHF	LBFH

❹ What is the probability that you would draw, in any order, a frog, a lion, and a bird card as the first three cards?

F. $\dfrac{1}{24}$ G. $\dfrac{6}{24}$ H. $\dfrac{8}{24}$ I. $\dfrac{24}{24}$

❺ What is the likelihood that you could predict the exact order in which the cards would be selected?

A. unlikely   B. likely   C. certain   D. impossible

Name: _____

6 Which probability statement is true?

    F. It is impossible to select a 2 of hearts from a full deck of cards.

    G. It is likely that when you flip a coin 10 times it will show heads at least once.

    H. It is unlikely that you will blink in the next 24 hours.

    I. It is certain that the results of 2 rolls of a die will be different.

7 Is the following statement true or false?

> You are as likely to roll the number 1 as you are to roll the number 6 using a number cube with the numbers 1-6 on it.

True or false? _____

Explain your thinking. _____

_____

8 Use the picture of the spinner to answer the question.

Make an organizer (list, table, chart, or tree diagram) showing all the possible outcomes for sums made by adding two spins.

Example: A spin of 2 then 3 would be a sum of 5.
So 2 + 3 = 5 is one possible outcome.

Remember: A spin of 2 then 3 is different than a spin of 3 then 2.

Use the organizer you made in question 8 to answer questions 9 and 10.

9 What is the total number of possible outcomes for two spins? _____

Explain your thinking. _____

_____

10 In fraction form, write the probability of spinning each sum. The first two are done for you.

The sum is 2: $\dfrac{1}{16}$ The sum is 4: _____   The sum is 6: _____

The sum is 3: $\dfrac{2}{16}$ The sum is 5: _____   The sum is 7: _____

Topic 7, Subtopic 2 Assessment:
Statistics

Use the following information to answer questions 1-3.

Phil and Scott wanted to see who was the better bowler. They decided that five games would be enough to settle the matter. The table below lists their scores for each of the five games.

PHIL AND SCOTT'S BOWLING CONTEST

	Game 1	Game 2	Game 3	Game 4	Game 5
Phil	72	84	156	109	84
Scott	84	102	80	254	156

❶ What is the mode for all ten games played?

A. 10   C. 156

B. 84   D. no mode

❷ What is the median score for Scott's games?

F. 84   H. 135

G. 102   I. 300

❸ What is the mean score for Phil's games?

A. 33   C. 101

B. 84   D. 505

Use the line graph and a calculator to answer questions 4-6.

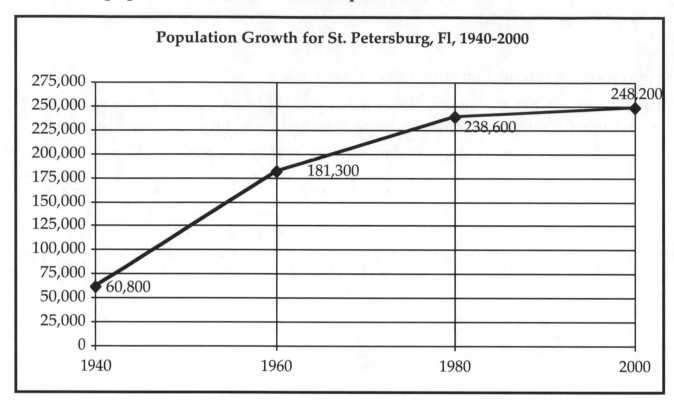

Population Growth for St. Petersburg, Fl, 1940-2000

4 What is the range of the data?

    F. 728,900   **G.** 275,000   **H.** 187,400   **I.** 182,225

5 Which statement is the most accurate interpretation of the data?

    A. The greatest 20-year growth in population was from 1980 to 2000.

    B. The population increased by about 20,000 from 1940 to 1960.

    C. The range of population was about 190,000 over 60 years.

    D. There was less growth from 1960 to 1980 than from 1980 to 2000.

6 To estimate the population for 1950, Troy found the mean of the data for 1940 and 1960. What number did Troy find for the estimated population in 1950?

    F. 60,525   **G.** 121,050   **H.** 181,300   **I.** 209,950

Name: _____

7 Seven families were discussing how long each had lived in the neighborhood. This data set shows the number of years that six families had lived there.

29	25	53	43	12	53

The seventh family had lived in the neighborhood 30 years. Is the following statement true or false?

30 years is the median for the set of data.

True or false? _____

Explain your thinking. _____

_____

8 The following numbers represent the ages of six teachers at Hill Elementary School.

29	57	43	68	69

The principal stated that their median age is 43.

Is her statement true or false? _____

Explain your thinking. _____

_____

Use the following graph to answer questions 9 and 10.

The following bar graph displays prices from "Nutz & Stuff" and the "Wholesale Nut Co." The prices are based on a five-pound order.

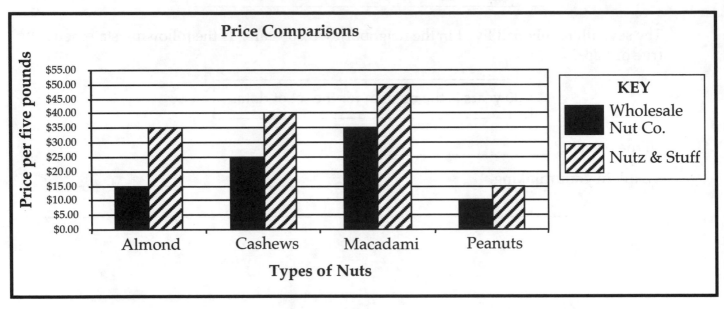

9 If you wanted to purchase a large number of nuts at the lowest price,

which company would you go to? _____

  Explain your thinking using the data in the bar graph. _____

  _____

  _____

10 Use a calculator for this question. What is the difference between the average price of nuts at the Wholesale Nut Co. and Nutz & Stuff?

10a. Price Difference: _____

10b. Write a statement that summarizes your findings. _____

  _____

10c. Explain the procedure you followed, using a calculator. _____

  _____

  _____

Topic 7, Subtopic 2 Assessment:
Statistics – Additional Items for Benchmark *MA.E.3.2.1*

---

❶ Andy is collecting data for a project about health in his science class. He wants to know how many glasses of water each member of his class drinks. Which of the following surveys would be best for Andy to collect his data?

A.

WHAT WE DRINK
Please check all the beverages you drink.
☐ Water   ☐ Soda
☐ Milk   ☐ Juice

B.

BEVERAGES WE LIKE
Please number the following beverages 1-4 in the order you like them, 1 being your favorite and 4 your least favorite.
___ Water   ___ Soda
___ Milk   ___ Juice

C.

HOW MUCH WATER WE DRINK
1. Do you drink water during an average day? yes/no _____
2. If yes, how many glasses of water do you drink each day? _____

D.

WHAT I WANT RIGHT NOW
If you could have a drink right now, please check the beverage you'd want.
☐ Water   ☐ Soda
☐ Milk   ☐ Juice

Use the following chart to answer questions 2 and 3.

Glasses of Water that Students Drink Each Day	
Zero glasses		
One glass	⁴⁄⁄⁄
Two glasses	⁴⁄⁄⁄	
Three glasses	|||
Four glasses	||

❷   While working with his data, Andy wrote the following in his notes.

> 0, 1, 1, 1, 1, 1, 2, 2, 2, 2, 2, 2, 3, 3, 3, 4, 4

What statistical measure was Andy most likely trying to find?

A. median   C. mean

B. mode   D. range

❸   After filling out his survey, Andy's classmate Rob claimed that he drinks at least 5 more glasses of water a day than anyone else in the class.

Is he right? Yes or no? _____

Which statistical measure (mean, median, mode, or range) did you use in

determining so, and how did you use it? _____

_____

_____

Name: _____

Use the following chart to answer questions 4 and 5.

Our Favorite Types of Exercise	
Basketball	ⵉ ⵉ ⵉ ⵉ ⵉ ⵉ ⵉ ⵉ ⵉ ⵉ ⵉ ⵉ ⵉ
Swimming	ⵉ ⵉ ⵉ ⵉ ⵉ ⵉ ⵉ ⵉ ⵉ ⵉ
Football	ⵉ ⵉ ⵉ ⵉ ⵉ ⵉ ⵉ ⵉ ⵉ
Running	ⵉ ⵉ ⵉ ⵉ ⵉ
Tennis	ⵉ ⵉ ⵉ
Gymnastics	ⵉ ⵉ

4 For his science project about health, Russ designed a survey to find what was the most popular form of exercise with his classmates. The above tally chart shows the data Russ gathered with his survey. What would be the best type of graph to display this information?

    A. line graph

    B. bar graph

    C. double-bar graph

    D. scatter plot

5 Using the above tally chart, make a graph showing Russ's results. Be sure to include a title as well as a label and scale for each axis.

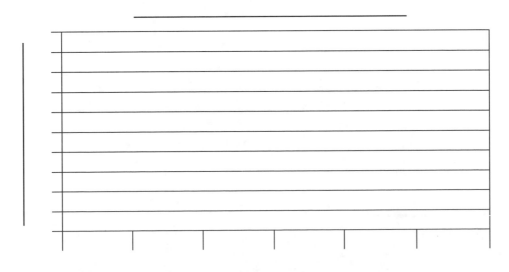